ITALIAN
FOR EVERYONE
JUNIOR
5 WORDS A DAY

FREE AUDIO
website and app

www.dk5words.com/uk

ITALIAN
FOR EVERYONE
JUNIOR

5 WORDS A DAY

FREE AUDIO
website and app

www.dk5words.com/uk

DK

For the curious

Penguin Random House

DK LONDON
Project Editors Sophie Adam, Elizabeth Blakemore
Project Art Editor Anna Scully
Designer Annabel Schick
Illustrators Amy Child, Gus Scott
Managing Editor Christine Stroyan
Managing Art Editor Anna Hall
Production Editor Kavita Varma
Production Controller Samantha Cross
Senior Jacket Designer Suhita Dharamjit
Jacket Design Development Manager Sophia MTT
Publisher Andrew Macintyre
Art Director Karen Self
Publishing Director Jonathan Metcalf

Translation Andiamo! Language Services Ltd

DK INDIA
Pre-Production Manager Sunil Sharma
DTP Designers Manish Chandra Upreti,
Umesh Singh Rawat

First published in Great Britain in 2021 by
Dorling Kindersley Limited
DK, One Embassy Gardens,
8 Viaduct Gardens,
London, SW11 7BW

The authorised representative in the EEA is
Dorling Kindersley Verlag GmbH. Arnulfstr. 124,
80636 Munich, Germany

Copyright © 2021
Dorling Kindersley Limited
A Penguin Random House Company
10 9 8 7 6 5 4 3 2 1
001–323273–Jul/2021

All rights reserved.
No part of this publication may be reproduced,
stored in or introduced into a retrieval system,
or transmitted, in any form, or by any means
(electronic, mechanical, photocopying,
recording, or otherwise), without the prior
written permission of the copyright owner.

A CIP catalogue record for this book
is available from the British Library.
ISBN: 978-0-2414-9140-9

Printed and bound in China

For the curious
www.dk.com

This book was made with Forest
Stewardship Council ™ certified
paper – one small step in DK's
commitment to a sustainable future.
For more information go to
www.dk.com/our-green-pledge

Contents

How to use this book   6

Week 1	8	Week 13	56
Week 2	12	Week 14	60
Week 3	16	Week 15	64
Week 4	20	Week 16	68
Week 5	24	Week 17	72
Week 6	28	Week 18	76
Week 7	32	Week 19	80
Week 8	36	Week 20	84
Week 9	40	Week 21	88
Week 10	44	Week 22	92
Week 11	48	Week 23	96
Week 12	52	Week 24	100

Week 25	104	Week 37	152	Week 49	200
Week 26	108	Week 38	156	Week 50	204
Week 27	112	Week 39	160	Week 51	208
Week 28	116	Week 40	164	Week 52	212
Week 29	120	Week 41	168	Numbers	216
Week 30	124	Week 42	172	Days and months	217
Week 31	128	Week 43	176	English word list	218
Week 32	132	Week 44	180	Italian word list	224
Week 33	136	Week 45	184	Common subjects	231
Week 34	140	Week 46	188	Answers	232
Week 35	144	Week 47	192	Acknowledgments	240
Week 36	148	Week 48	196		

How to use this book

Italian for Everyone Junior: 5 Words a Day is a vocabulary book for children that teaches and tests more than 1,000 Italian words. Words are taught in weekly units of 5 days.

Learning new vocabulary

On Days 1–4, the child will be presented with 20 new words, which are taught 5 words at a time through colourful illustrations.

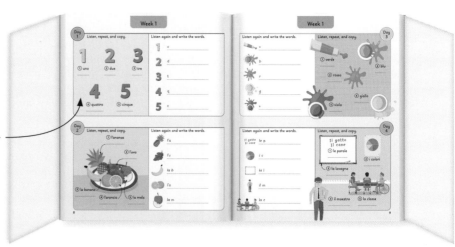

1 First, listen to the words on the audio app or website, repeat the words out loud, and then write them out in the space below each word.

Masculine and feminine words

In Italian, all nouns (things or people) are either masculine or feminine. Many words have "il", "l", "lo", "la", "i", "gli", or "le" in front of them. These all mean "the" in English. Words that appear after "il", "lo", "i", or "gli" are usually masculine. Words that follow "la" or "le" are usually feminine. Plural nouns appear after "i", "gli", or "le", and singular nouns appear after "il", "lo", "l", or "la".

2 Next, use the book flaps to cover the illustrations and listen to the words again.

3 With the words still covered, try writing out each word from memory.

Testing new vocabulary

On Day 5, the child can practise the 20 new words and reinforce their learning through fun exercises.

A variety of exercises are used to test all 20 words.

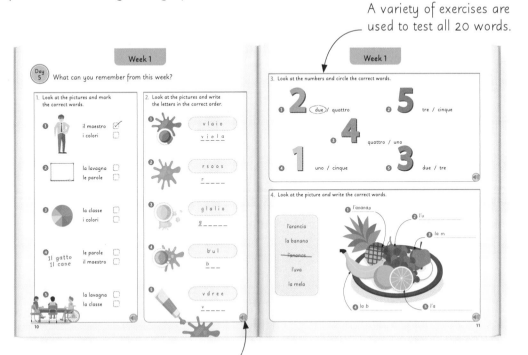

Once you have finished an exercise, listen to the words again on the app or website.

Answers to all the questions are given at the back of the book.

Audio

Pronunciation is an important aspect of learning a new language. Audio for all the words in this book is available on the **DK 5 Words** website and app. You should encourage your child to listen to the audio and repeat the words out loud. Access the audio recordings for free at **www.dk5words.com/uk** or download the **DK 5 Words** app from the App Store or Google Play.

FREE AUDIO
website and app

www.dk5words.com/uk

Week 1

A+

Day 1

Listen, repeat, and copy.

1 2 3

① uno — uno

② due — due

③ tre — tre

4 5

④ quattro — quattro

⑤ cinque — cinque

Listen again and write the words.

1 u uno

2 d due

3 t tre

4 q uattro

5 cinque

Day 2

Listen, repeat, and copy.

① l'ananas — l'ananas

② l'uva — l'uva

③ la banana — la banana

④ l'arancia — l'arancia

⑤ la mela — la mela

Listen again and write the words.

l'ananas

l'uva

la banana

l'arancia

la mela

Listen again and write the words.

 v _erde_

 b _lu_

 r _osso_

 gi _llo_

 vi _ola_

Listen, repeat, and copy.

① verde
verde

② blu
blu

③ rosso
rosso

④ giallo
giallo

⑤ viola
viola

Listen again and write the words.

 Il gatto Il cane   le _parole_

 i c _olori_

 la l _avagna_

 il m _aestro_

la c _lasse_

Listen, repeat, and copy.

Il gatto
Il cane

① le parole
le parde

② i colori
i colori

③ la lavagna
la lavagn

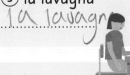

④ il maestro
il maestro

⑤ la classe
la classe

9

What can you remember from this week?

1. Look at the pictures and mark the correct words.

1

il maestro ☑
i colori ☐

2

la lavagna ☐
le parole ☑

3

la classe ☐
i colori ☑

4
Il gatto
Il cane

le parole ☑
il maestro ☐

5

la lavagna ☐
la classe ☑

2. Look at the pictures and write the letters in the correct order.

1

v l a i o

v i o l a

2

r s o o s

r o s s o

3

g l a l i o

g a l l i o

4

b u l

b l u

5

v d r e e

v e r d e

3. Look at the numbers and circle the correct words.

2
① ⟨due⟩ / quattro

5
② tre / ⟨cinque⟩

4
③ ⟨quattro⟩ / uno

1
④ ⟨uno⟩ / cinque

3
⑤ due / ⟨tre⟩

4. Look at the picture and write the correct words.

la' arancia

l'arancia

la banana

~~l'ananas~~

l'uva

la mela

① l'ananas

② l'u va

③ la m τ l a

④ la b anana

⑤ l'a rancia

11

Day 1

Listen, repeat, and copy.

6
① sei
sei

7
② sette
sette

8
③ otto
otto

9
④ nove
Nove

10
⑤ dieci
dieci

Listen again and write the words.

6 s e i

7 s e t t e

8 o t t o

9 n o v e

10 d i e c i

Day 2

Listen, repeat, and copy.

12345

② i numeri
i numeri

Aa	Bb	Cc	Dd	Ee
Ff	Gg	Hh	Ii	Jj
Kk	Ll	Mm	Nn	Oo
Pp	Qq	Rr	Ss	Tt
Uu	Vv	Ww	Xx	Yy
Zz				

① la classe
la crasse

③ l'alfabeto
l'alfabeto

④ le lettere
le tettere

⑤ la compagna di classe
la compagna di classe

Listen again and write the words.

la classe

12345 i numeri

l'alfabeto

le lettere

la compagnadicl usse

A+

Day 3

Listen again and write the words.

il b urattino

la s tatuetta

l'o rsetto

il g ioco da tavolo

la bambola

Listen, repeat, and copy.

① il burattino
il burattino

② la statuetta
la statuetta

③ l'orsetto
l'orsetto

④ il gioco da tavolo
il gioco da tavolo

⑤ la bambola
la bambola

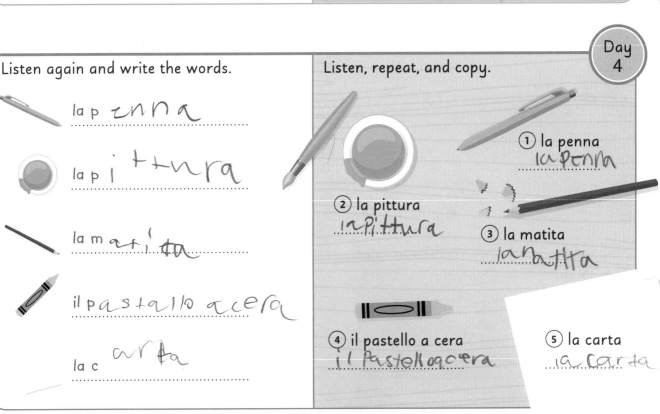

Day 4

Listen again and write the words.

la p enna

la p ittura

la m atita

il pastallo acera

la c arta

Listen, repeat, and copy.

① la penna
la penna

② la pittura
la pittura

③ la matita
la matita

④ il pastello a cera
il pastello a cera

⑤ la carta
la carta

Week 2

What can you remember from this week?

---

1. Look at the pictures and write the correct words.

~~l'alfabeto~~   ~~i numeri~~   la compagna di classe   ~~le lettere~~   ~~la classe~~

12345

① i numeri

② l'a lfaroleto

③ le l ettero

④ la c ompagnadiclas ⑤ la classc

---

2. Match the pictures to the correct words.

① ② ③ ④ ⑤

l'orsetto   la bambola   la statuetta   il burattino   il gioco da tavolo

14

A+

3. Read the words and mark the correct pictures.

1 la penna   A ☐   B ☑

2 il pastello a cera   A ☑   B ☐

3 la carta   A ☐   B ☑

4 la pittura   A ☑   B ☐

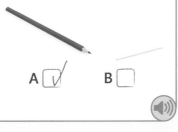

5 la matita   A ☑   B ☐

4. Look at the numbers and fill in the missing letters.

1 o t t o

2 s e i

3  n o v e

4 s e t t e

5  d i e c i

A+

Day 1

Listen, repeat, and copy.

11
① undici
undici

12
② dodici
dodici

13
③ tredici
tredici

14
④ quattordici
quattordici

15
⑤ quindici
quindici

Listen again and write the words.

11 *undici*

12 *dodici*

13 *tredici*

14 *quattordici*

15 *quindici*

Day 2

Listen, repeat, and copy.

① la scuola — *la scuola*
② la casa — *la casa*
③ la strada — *lastrada*
④ il parco — *il parco*
⑤ il cortile — *il cortile*

Listen again and write the words.

 la s *cuola*

 la c *asa*

 la s *trada*

 il p *arco*

 il c *ortile*

A+

Listen again and write the words.

 la f **a m i g l i a**

 il p **a d r e**

 la m **a d r e**

 il f **i g l i o**

 la f **i g l i a**

Listen, repeat, and copy.

① la famiglia
la famiglia

② il padre
il Padre

③ la madre
la madre

④ il figlio
il figlio

⑤ la figlia
la figlia

Listen again and write the words.

d **i s e g n a r e**

c **o n t a r e**

Il gatto f **a r e l o s p e l l i n g**

c **o l o r a r e**

s **s c r i v e r e**

Listen, repeat, and copy.

① disegnare
disegnare

Il gatto

② contare
ontare

③ fare lo spelling
fare lo spelling

④ colorare
colorare

⑤ scrivere
scriver

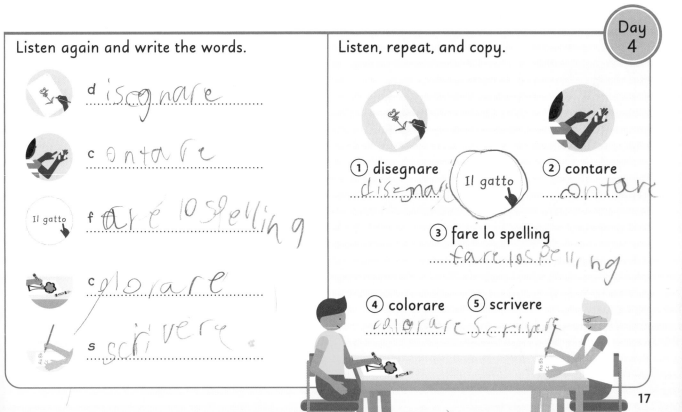

17

Day 5

What can you remember from this week?

1. Look at the pictures and mark the correct words.

1
- disegnare ☑
- fare lo spelling ☐

2
- colorare ☑
- contare ☐

3
- contare ☑
- scrivere ☐

4 Il gatto
- colorare ☐
- fare lo spelling ☑

5
- disegnare ☐
- scrivere ☑

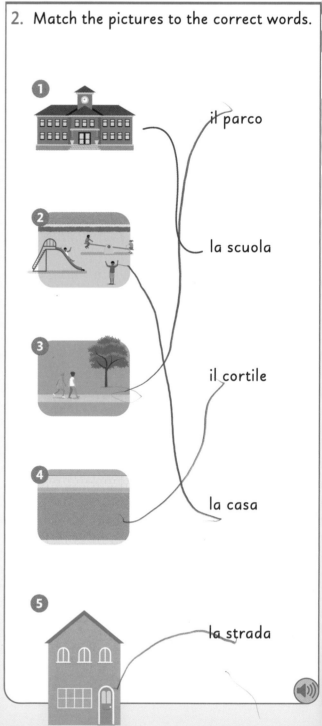

2. Match the pictures to the correct words.

1 — il parco

2 — la scuola

3 — il cortile

4 — la casa

5 — la strada

3. Look at the numbers and write the correct words.

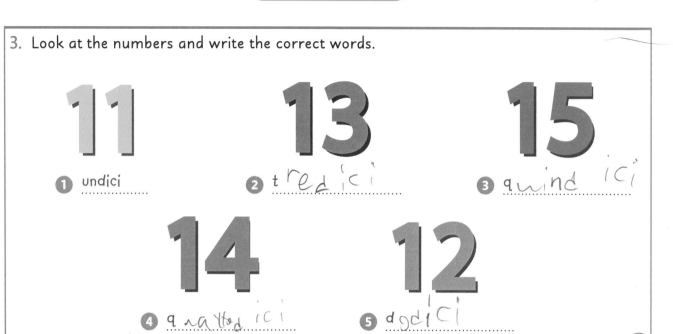

11
① undici

13
② t red ici

15
③ quind ici

14
④ q na yto ici

12
⑤ d 0 d i ci

4. Look at the pictures and write the correct words.

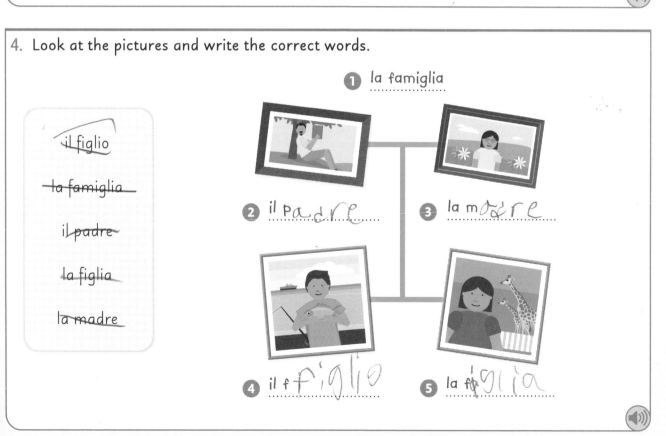

① la famiglia

il figlio

~~la famiglia~~

~~il padre~~

~~la figlia~~

~~la madre~~

② il padre

③ la madre

④ il figlio

⑤ la figlia

Day 1

Listen, repeat, and copy.

16 ① sedici
....

17 ② diciassette
....

18 ③ diciotto
....

19 ④ diciannove
....

20 ⑤ venti
....

Listen again and write the words.

16 s ....

17 d ....

18 d ....

19 d ....

20 v ....

Day 2

Listen, repeat, and copy.

① la mucca
....

② la capra
....

③ la pecora
....

④ la gallina
....

⑤ il cavallo
....

Listen again and write the words.

 la m ....

la c ....

 la p ....

la g ....

 il c ....

Listen again and write the words.

la c ....

il b ....

il s ....

la s ....

la c ....

Listen, repeat, and copy.

① la camera da letto
....

② il bagno
....

③ il soggiorno
....

④ la sala da pranzo
....

⑤ la cucina
....

Listen again and write the words.

n ....

b ....

m ....

r ....

a ....

Listen, repeat, and copy.

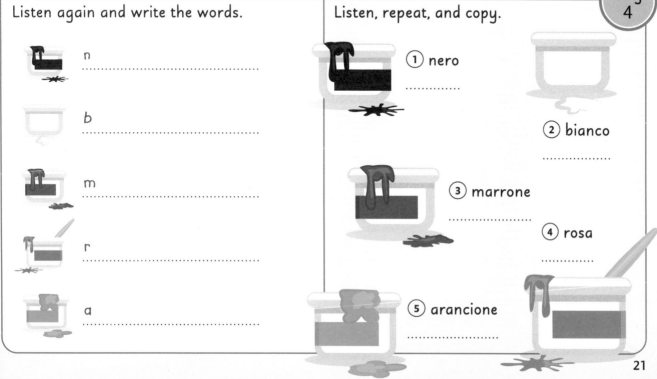

① nero
....

② bianco
....

③ marrone
....

④ rosa
....

⑤ arancione
....

Day 5 What can you remember from this week?

1. Look at the pictures and fill in the missing letters.

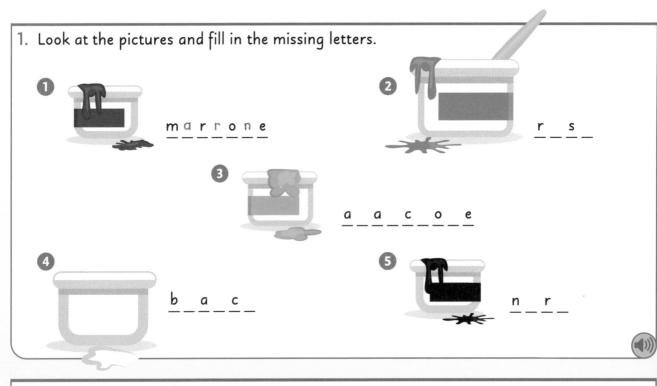

① m a r r o n e

② r _ s _

③ a _ a _ c _ o _ e

④ b _ a _ c _

⑤ n _ r _

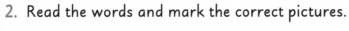

2. Read the words and mark the correct pictures.

① la camera da letto

A ☐   B ✓

② la cucina

A ☐   B ☐

③ il bagno

A ☐   B ☐

④ il soggiorno

A ☐   B ☐

⑤ la sala da pranzo

A ☐   B ☐

3. Look at the pictures and mark the correct words.

1. la mucca ☐
   la gallina ☑
   la pecora ☐

2. la gallina ☐
   la capra ☐
   il cavallo ☐

3. la pecora ☐
   la mucca ☐
   il cavallo ☐

4. la capra ☐
   la gallina ☐
   la mucca ☐

5. il cavallo ☐
   la pecora ☐
   la capra ☐

4. Look at the numbers and write the letters in the correct order.

1. 17
   d s a t s i c i e t e
   d i c i a s s e t t e

2. 20
   v t n i e
   v _ _ _ _ _

3. 18
   d i t c i o o t
   d _ _ _ _ _ _ _ _

4. 16
   s i d i c e
   s _ _ _ _ _ _

5. 19
   d n n i v c i a e o
   d _ _ _ _ _ _ _ _ _

Day 1

Listen, repeat, and copy.

1. la zebra
   ....
2. la giraffa
   ....
3. il leone
   ....
4. l'ippopotamo
   ....
5. l'elefante
   ....

Listen again and write the words.

la z ....

la g ....

il l ....

l'i ....

l'e ....

Day 2

Listen, repeat, and copy.

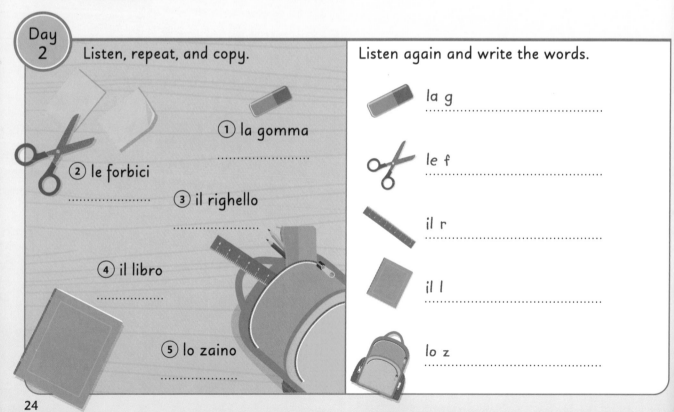

1. la gomma
   ....
2. le forbici
   ....
3. il righello
   ....
4. il libro
   ....
5. lo zaino
   ....

Listen again and write the words.

la g ....

le f ....

il r ....

il l ....

lo z ....

Day 3

Listen again and write the words.

r ....

a ....

i ....

i ....

i ....

Listen, repeat, and copy.

① rispondere
....

② ascoltare
....

③ imparare
....

④ insegnare
....

⑤ indicare
....

Day 4

Listen again and write the words.

il m ....

la p ....

il k ....

l'a ....

il c ....

Listen, repeat, and copy.

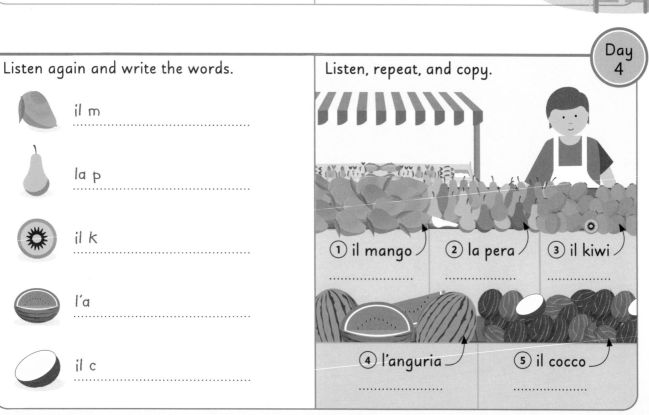

① il mango
....

② la pera
....

③ il kiwi
....

④ l'anguria
....

⑤ il cocco
....

25

Week 5

Day 5

What can you remember from this week?

1. Match the pictures to the correct words.

①   il leone

②   la zebra

③   l'elefante

④   l'ippopotamo

⑤   la giraffa

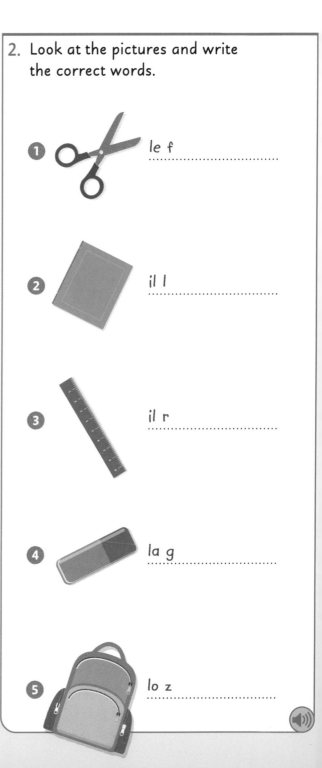

2. Look at the pictures and write the correct words.

①   le f ....

②   il l ....

③   il r ....

④   la g ....

⑤   lo z ....

3. Look at the pictures and write the correct words.

rispondere   ascoltare   indicare   insegnare   imparare

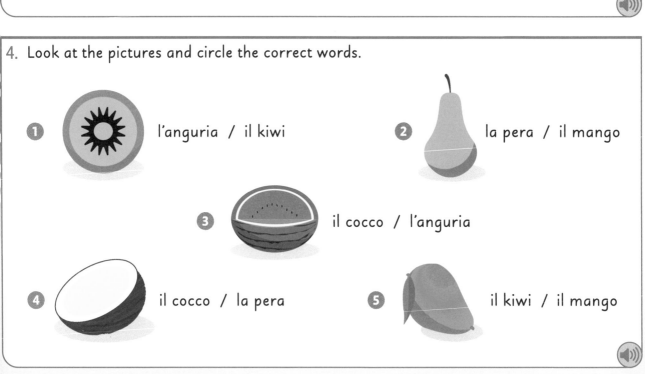

1 a ....

2 i ....

3 i ....

4 i ....

5 r ....

4. Look at the pictures and circle the correct words.

1 l'anguria / il kiwi

2 la pera / il mango

3 il cocco / l'anguria

4 il cocco / la pera

5 il kiwi / il mango

Day 1

Listen, repeat, and copy.

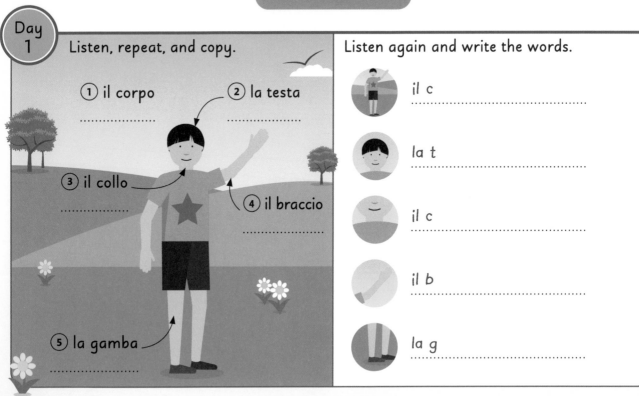

① il corpo

② la testa

③ il collo

④ il braccio

⑤ la gamba

Listen again and write the words.

il c ....

la t ....

il c ....

il b ....

la g ....

Day 2

Listen, repeat, and copy.

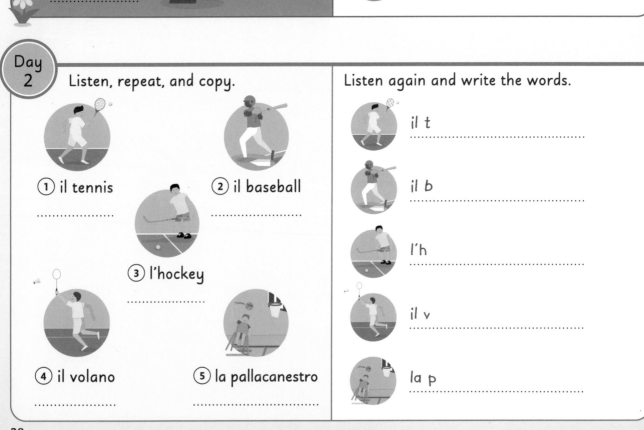

① il tennis

② il baseball

③ l'hockey

④ il volano

⑤ la pallacanestro

Listen again and write the words.

il t ....

il b ....

l'h ....

il v ....

la p ....

Week 6

Listen again and write the words.

il g ....

l'a ....

la n ....

il m ....

la p ....

Listen, repeat, and copy.

① il gabbiano
....

② l'aquilone
....

③ la nave
....

④ il mare
....

⑤ la palla
....

Listen again and write the words.

il c ....

il g ....

il p ....

il c ....

g ....

Listen, repeat, and copy.

① il cane
....

② il gatto
....

③ il pesce rosso
....

④ il coniglio
....

⑤ gli animali domestici
....

Week 6

Day 5 What can you remember from this week?

---

1. Read the words and mark the correct pictures.

1 il gatto

A ☐   B ☐

2 il coniglio

A ☐   B ☐

3 il cane

A ☐   B ☐

4 gli animali domestici

A ☐   B ☐

5 il pesce rosso

A ☐   B ☐

---

2. Look at the pictures and fill in the missing letters.

1    l _ t _ _ s _ a

2   _ a _ _ a _ b _

3    i _ _ c _ r _ o

4   _ l _ r _ c _ i _

5    i _ _ c _ l _ o

Week 6

3. Look at the pictures and mark the correct words.

1. il baseball ☐
   l'hockey ☐

2. il tennis ☐
   il volano ☐

3. la pallacanestro ☐
   il baseball ☐

4. il tennis ☐
   la pallacanestro ☐

5. il volano ☐
   l'hockey ☐

4. Look at the pictures and write the correct words.

1. il m ....

2. il g ....

3. l'a ....

4. la n ....

5. la p ....

31

Day 1

Listen, repeat, and copy.

① i vestiti
....

② i calzini
....

③ il pigiama
....

④ i jeans
....

⑤ la biancheria intima
....

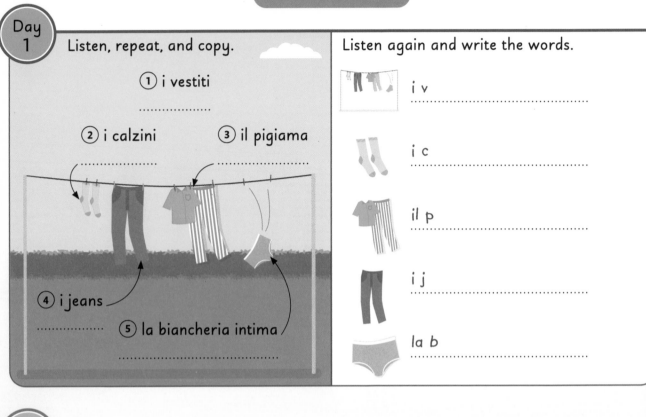

Listen again and write the words.

i v ....

i c ....

il p ....

i j ....

la b ....

Day 2

Listen, repeat, and copy.

① il bambino
....

② la bambina
....

③ il bebè
....

④ l'uomo
....

⑤ la donna
....

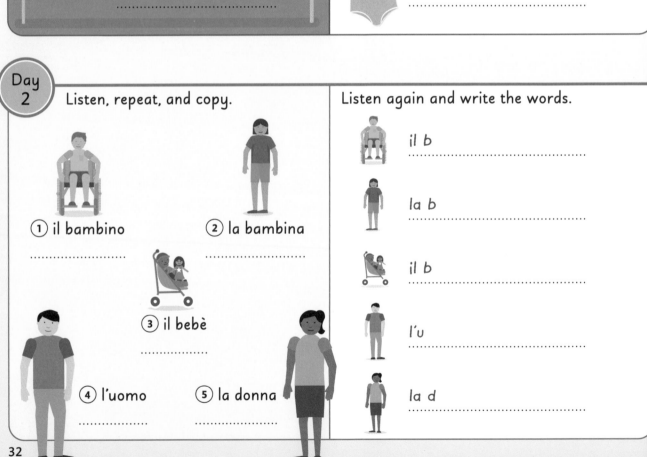

Listen again and write the words.

il b ....

la b ....

il b ....

l'u ....

la d ....

Listen again and write the words.

l'h ....

la p ....

il p ....

le p ....

i n ....

Listen, repeat, and copy.

① l'hamburger
....

② la pizza
....

③ il pollo
....

④ le patatine fritte
....

⑤ i noodle
....

Listen again and write the words.

la t ....

la p ....

la l ....

il t ....

il d ....

Listen, repeat, and copy.

① la televisione
....

② la poltrona
....

③ la libreria
....

④ il tappeto
....

⑤ il divano
....

Day 5

What can you remember from this week?

1. Look at the pictures and fill in the missing letters.

① l _ b m i a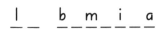

② l' _ o _ o

③ _ _ l _ a _ b _ n _

④ i _ b _ b _

⑤ l _ d _ n _ a

2. Read the words and mark the correct pictures.

① i jeans A ☐ B ☐

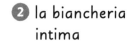

② la biancheria intima A ☐ B ☐

③ il pigiama A ☐ B ☐

④ i calzini A ☐ B ☐

⑤ i vestiti A ☐ B ☐

3. Look at the pictures and write the correct words.

> il tappeto   il divano   la televisione   la libreria   la poltrona

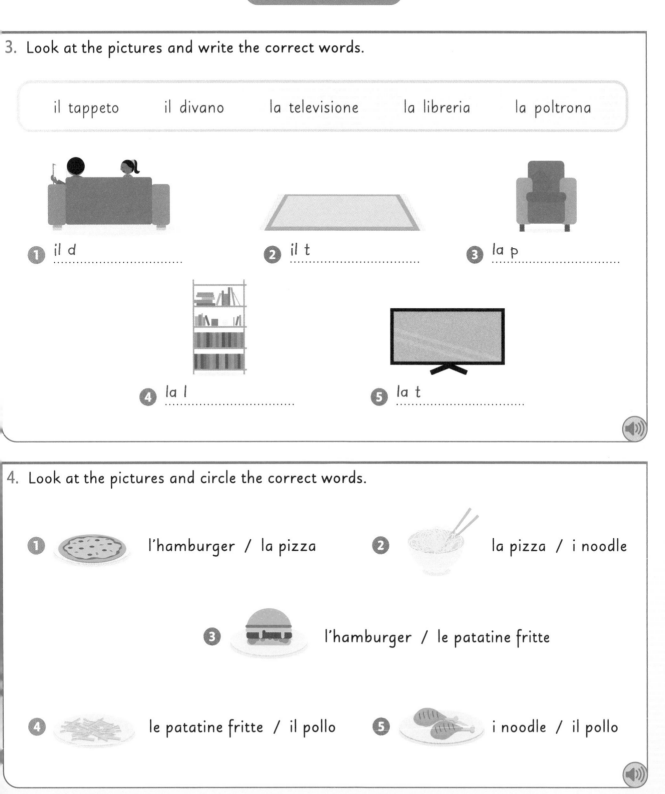

① il d ....

② il t ....

③ la p ....

④ la l ....

⑤ la t ....

4. Look at the pictures and circle the correct words.

① l'hamburger / la pizza

② la pizza / i noodle

③ l'hamburger / le patatine fritte

④ le patatine fritte / il pollo

⑤ i noodle / il pollo

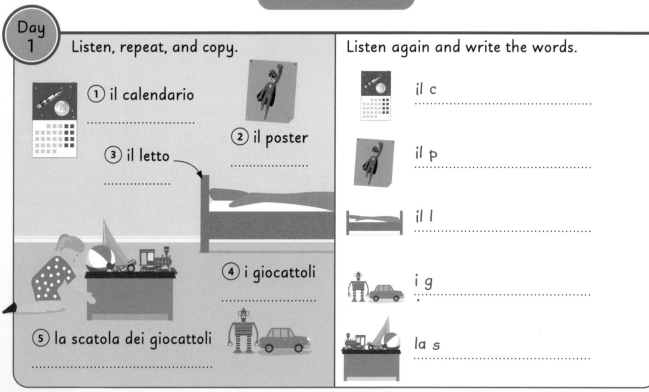

Day 1

Listen, repeat, and copy.

① il calendario

② il poster

③ il letto

④ i giocattoli

⑤ la scatola dei giocattoli

Listen again and write the words.

il c

il p

il l

i g

la s

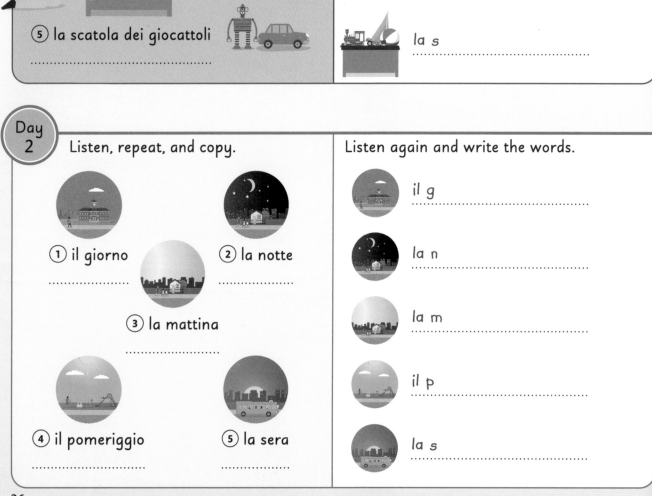

Day 2

Listen, repeat, and copy.

① il giorno

② la notte

③ la mattina

④ il pomeriggio

⑤ la sera

Listen again and write the words.

il g

la n

la m

il p

la s

Week 8

Listen again and write the words.

a ....

c ....

r ....

s ....

a ....

Listen, repeat, and copy.

① aprire
....

② chiudere
....

③ raccogliere
....

④ sedersi
....

⑤ alzarsi
....

Listen again and write the words.

la g ....

la s ....

la t ....

l'o ....

la r ....

Listen, repeat, and copy.

① la giungla
....

② la scimmia
....

③ la tigre
....

④ l'orso
....

⑤ la rana
....

Day 5

What can you remember from this week?

1. Look at the pictures and write the correct words.

1 la t _____

2 la r _____

3 la s _____

4 la g _____

5 l'o _____

2. Read the words and mark the correct pictures.

1 il poster
A ☐   B ☐

2 il calendario
A ☐   B ☐

3 il letto
A ☐   B ☐

4 la scatola dei giocattoli
A ☐   B ☐

5 i giocattoli
A ☐   B ☐

Week 8

3. Look at the pictures and fill in the missing letters.

 s _ d _ r _ i

 a _ r _ r _

 c _ i _ d _ r _

 r _ c _ o _ l _ e _ e

 a _ z _ r _ i

4. Look at the pictures and mark the correct words.

 il pomeriggio ☐
la sera ☐

 la notte ☐
il pomeriggio ☐

 la notte ☐
la mattina ☐

 il giorno ☐
la sera ☐

 la mattina ☐
il giorno ☐

Day 1

Listen, repeat, and copy.

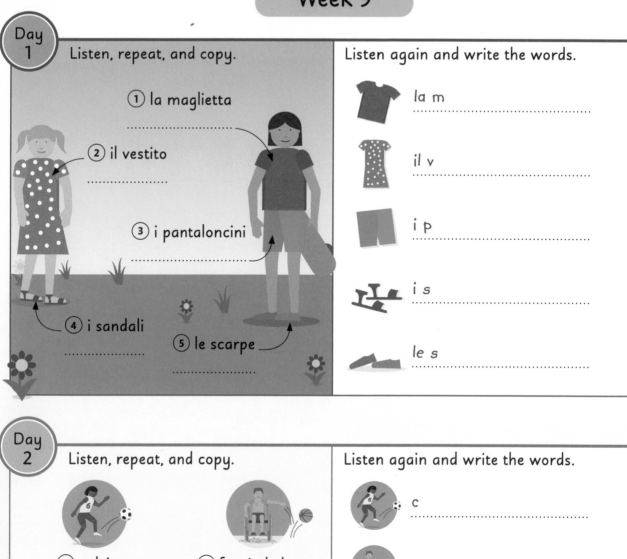

① la maglietta

② il vestito

③ i pantaloncini

④ i sandali

⑤ le scarpe

Listen again and write the words.

la m

il v

i p

i s

le s

Day 2

Listen, repeat, and copy.

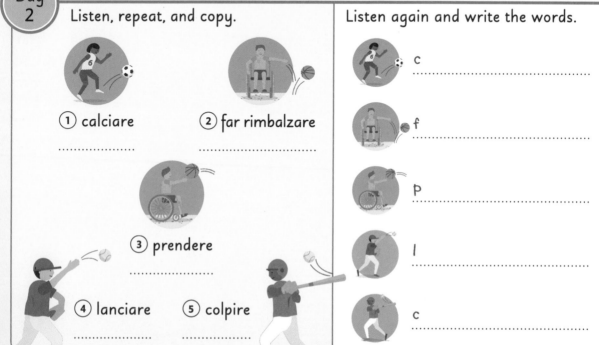

① calciare

② far rimbalzare

③ prendere

④ lanciare   ⑤ colpire

Listen again and write the words.

c

f

p

l

c

Listen again and write the words.

i n ....

la n ....

il n ....

il n ....

la n ....

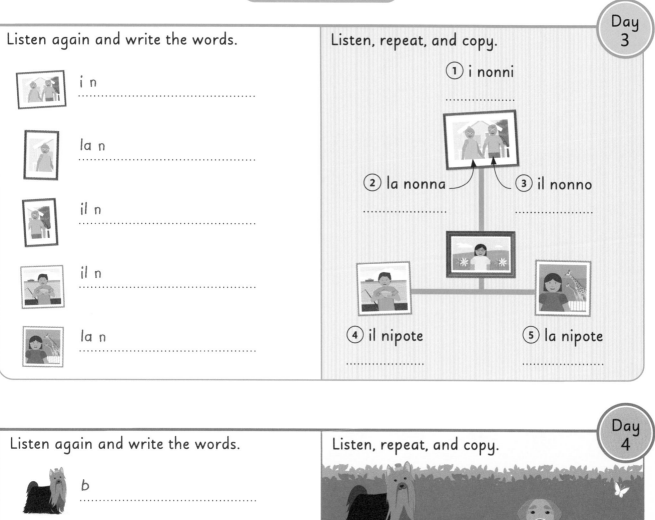

Listen, repeat, and copy.

① i nonni
....

② la nonna
....

③ il nonno
....

④ il nipote
....

⑤ la nipote
....

Listen again and write the words.

b ....

g ....

v ....

b ....

p ....

Listen, repeat, and copy.

① bello
....

② giovane
....

③ vecchio
....

④ buono
....

⑤ pauroso
....

41

Day 5

What can you remember from this week?

1. Look at the pictures and write the correct words.

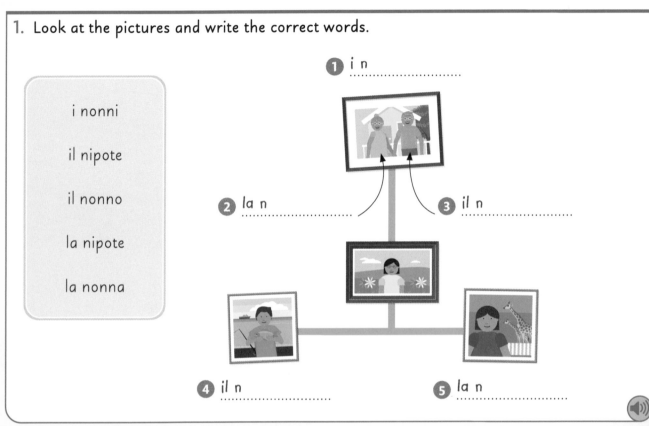

i nonni

il nipote

il nonno

la nipote

la nonna

1 i n ....

2 la n ....

3 il n ....

4 il n ....

5 la n ....

2. Match the pictures to the correct words.

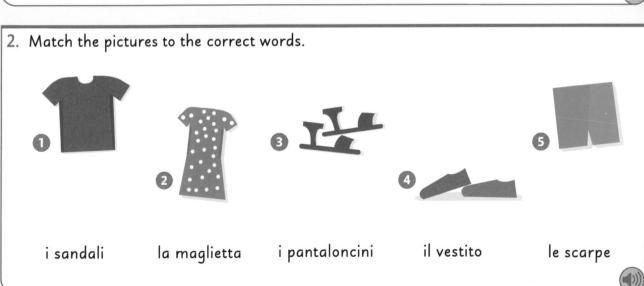

1   2   3   4   5

i sandali   la maglietta   i pantaloncini   il vestito   le scarpe

3. Look at the pictures and mark the correct words.

1. bello ☐
   vecchio ☐

2. pauroso ☐
   vecchio ☐

3. pauroso ☐
   buono ☐

4. bello ☐
   giovane ☐

5. buono ☐
   giovane ☐

4. Look at the pictures and write the correct words.

calciare   prendere   colpire
    lanciare   far rimbalzare

1. P..........................

2. c..........................

3. c..........................

4. l..........................

5. f..........................

Day 1

Listen, repeat, and copy.

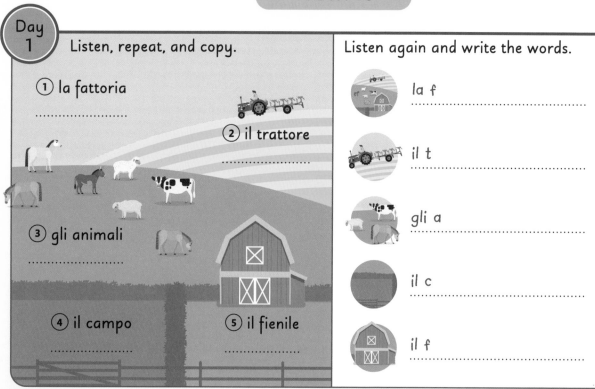

1. la fattoria
....

2. il trattore
....

3. gli animali
....

4. il campo
....

5. il fienile
....

Listen again and write the words.

la f ....

il t ....

gli a ....

il c ....

il f ....

Day 2

Listen, repeat, and copy.

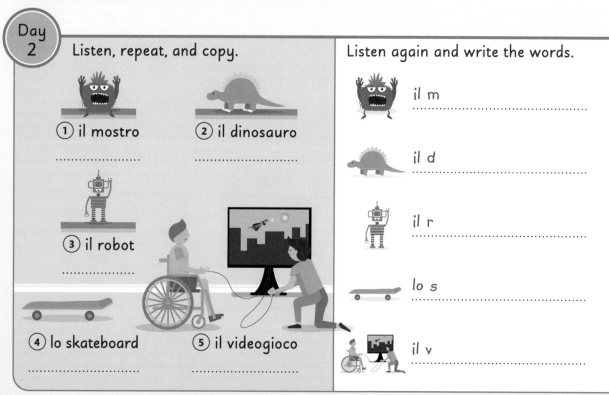

1. il mostro
....

2. il dinosauro
....

3. il robot
....

4. lo skateboard
....

5. il videogioco
....

Listen again and write the words.

il m ....

il d ....

il r ....

lo s ....

il v ....

Week 10

Day 3

Listen again and write the words.

c ....

c ....

s ....

s ....

a ....

Listen, repeat, and copy.

① cancellare ....

② cerchiare ....

③ spuntare ....

④ sommare ....

⑤ abbinare ....

Day 4

Listen again and write the words.

g ....

le p ....

le d ....

i b ....

la p ....

Listen, repeat, and copy.

① gli uomini ....

② le persone ....

③ le donne ....

④ i bambini ....

⑤ la persona ....

45

Day 5

What can you remember from this week?

1. Look at the pictures and write the letters in the correct order.

1
la prsonea

la p ....

2
le dneon

le d ....

3
i bmnibia

i b ....

4
le psoeern

le p ....

5
gli umioin

gli u ....

2. Read the words and mark the correct pictures.

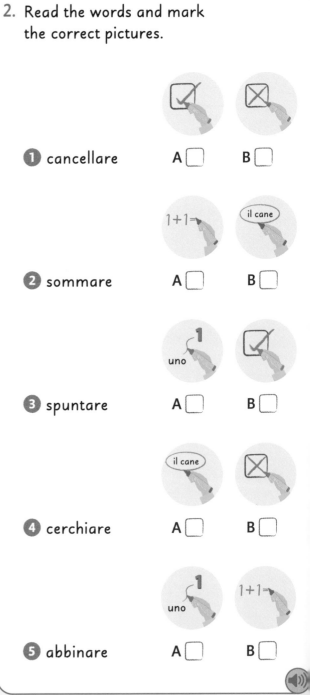

1 cancellare   A ☐   B ☐

2 sommare   A ☐   B ☐

3 spuntare   A ☐   B ☐

4 cerchiare   A ☐   B ☐

5 abbinare   A ☐   B ☐

3. Look at the pictures and write the correct words.

 il t ....

 il c ....

 la f ....

 gli a ....

 il f ....

4. Look at the pictures and circle the correct words.

 il dinosauro
il robot

 lo skateboard
il dinosauro

 il mostro
il videogioco

 il robot
il videogioco

 il mostro
lo skateboard

Week 11

Day 1

Listen, repeat, and copy.

① cantare

....

② danzare

....

③ suonare il pianoforte

....

④ suonare la chitarra

....

⑤ fare una foto

....

Listen again and write the words.

c ....

d ....

s ....

s ....

f ....

Day 2

Listen, repeat, and copy.

① pulito

....

② sporco

....

③ bello

....

④ grande

....

⑤ piccolo

....

Listen again and write the words.

p ....

s ....

b ....

g ....

p ....

Week 11

Listen again and write the words.

l'o
....

l'o
....

il v
....

le l
....

il n
....

Listen, repeat, and copy.

① l'occhio
....

② l'orecchio
....

③ il viso
....

④ le labbra
....

⑤ il naso
....

Listen again and write the words.

la c
....

la g
....

i p
....

il c
....

la g
....

Listen, repeat, and copy.

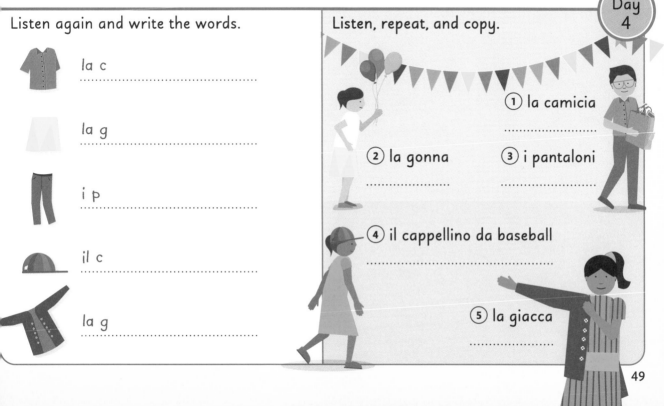

① la camicia
....

② la gonna
....

③ i pantaloni
....

④ il cappellino da baseball
....

⑤ la giacca
....

Week 11

Day 5

What can you remember from this week?

1. Look at the pictures and write the correct words.

1 l'o ....

2 le l ....

3 il n ....

4 l'o ....

5 il v ....

2. Read the words and mark the correct pictures.

1 cantare

A ☐ B ☐

2 suonare il pianoforte

A ☐ B ☐

3 danzare

A ☐ B ☐

4 suonare la chitarra

A ☐ B ☐

5 fare una foto

A ☐ B ☐

3. Look at the pictures and write the letters in the correct order.

1

b l o e l

b _ _ _ _ _

2

p t o i u l

p _ _ _ _ _ _

3

p l i o o c c

p _ _ _ _ _ _ _

4

s r p o c o

s _ _ _ _ _

5

g d e r a n

g _ _ _ _ _

4. Match the pictures to the correct words.

1

la gonna

2

la camicia

3

il cappellino da baseball

4

la giacca

5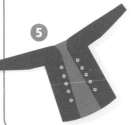

i pantaloni

Week 12

Day 1

Listen, repeat, and copy.

① la colazione

....

② l'uovo

....

③ i cereali

....

④ la salsiccia

....

⑤ il pancake

....

Listen again and write the words.

la c ....

l'u ....

i c ....

la s ....

il p ....

Day 2

Listen, repeat, and copy.

① felice

....

② triste

....

③ arrabbiata

....

④ impaurito

....

⑤ sorpresa

....

Listen again and write the words.

f ....

t ....

a ....

i ....

s ....

Listen again and write the words.

d ....

v ....

d ....

d ....

s ....

Listen, repeat, and copy.

① dentro ....

② vicino a ....

③ dietro ....

④ davanti ....

⑤ sopra ....

Listen again and write the words.

il c ....

il b ....

l'a ....

l'a ....

il p ....

Listen, repeat, and copy.

① il condominio ....

② il balcone ....

③ l'ascensore ....

④ l'appartamento ....

⑤ il piano terra ....

Week 12

Day 5

What can you remember from this week?

1. Look at the pictures and write the correct words.

> dentro   dietro   sopra
> davanti   vicino a

1. d ....

2. d ....

3. d ....

4. v ....

5. s ....

2. Look at the pictures and mark the correct words.

1.
i cereali ☐
l'uovo ☐

2.
il pancake ☐
la colazione ☐

3.
l'uovo ☐
la salsiccia ☐

4.
il pancake ☐
i cereali ☐

5.
la colazione ☐
la salsiccia ☐

3. Look at the pictures and circle the correct words.

① il balcone
il condominio

② l'appartamento
l'ascensore

③ il condominio
il piano terra

④ il piano terra
l'ascensore

⑤ il balcone
l'appartamento

4. Look at the pictures and fill in the missing letters.

① s _ r r _ s _

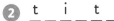
② _ t _ i _ t _

③ _ i _ p _ u _ _ i _ o

④ f _ l _ c _

⑤ a _ r _ b _ i _ t _

Day 1

Listen, repeat, and copy.

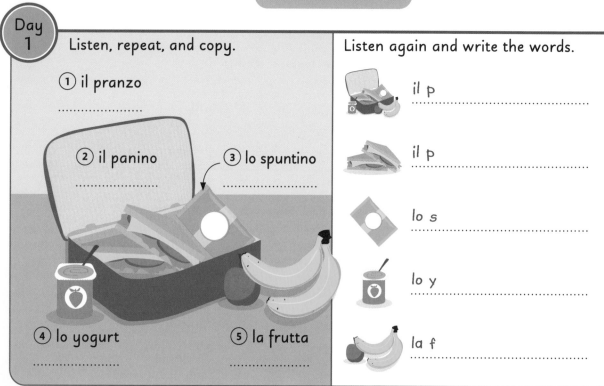

① il pranzo

② il panino

③ lo spuntino

④ lo yogurt

⑤ la frutta

Listen again and write the words.

il p ....

il p ....

lo s ....

lo y ....

la f ....

Day 2

Listen, repeat, and copy.

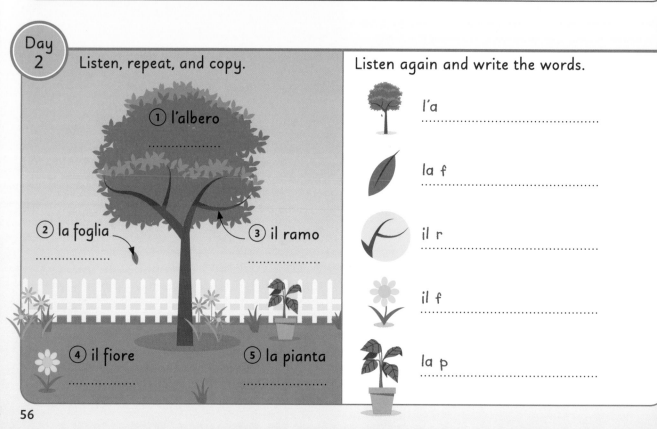

① l'albero

② la foglia

③ il ramo

④ il fiore

⑤ la pianta

Listen again and write the words.

l'a ....

la f ....

il r ....

il f ....

la p ....

Week 13

Listen again and write the words.

g ....

p ....

c ....

c ....

a ....

Listen, repeat, and copy.

① guidare

....

② prendere l'autobus

....

③ camminare

....

④ correre

....

⑤ andare
in bicicletta

....

Listen again and write the words.

la p ....

la t ....

il v ....

la n ....

l'a ....

Listen, repeat, and copy.

① la pioggia

....

② la tempesta

....

③ il vento

....

④ la nebbia

....

⑤ l'arcobaleno

....

Week 13

Day 5   What can you remember from this week?

---

1. Read the words and mark the correct pictures.

1 guidare

A ☐   B ☐

2 camminare

A ☐   B ☐

3 correre

A ☐   B ☐

4 prendere l'autobus

A ☐   B ☐

5 andare in bicicletta

A ☐   B ☐

---

2. Look at the pictures and write the correct words.

1 la f ....

2 il r ....

3 l'a ....

4 la p ....

5 il f ....

58

3. Look at the pictures and write the correct words.

la pioggia   la tempesta   il vento
l'arcobaleno   la nebbia

 la t _____

 il v _____

 la n _____

 la p _____

 l'a _____

4. Match the pictures to the correct words.

la frutta

lo spuntino

il pranzo

lo yogurt

il panino

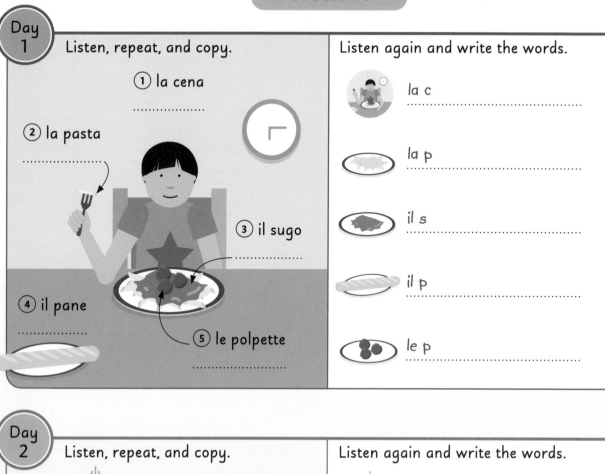

Day 1

Listen, repeat, and copy.

① la cena
....

② la pasta
....

③ il sugo
....

④ il pane
....

⑤ le polpette
....

Listen again and write the words.

la c ....

la p ....

il s ....

il p ....

le p ....

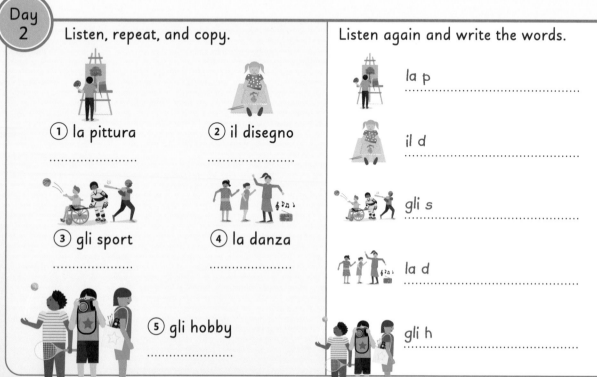

Day 2

Listen, repeat, and copy.

① la pittura
....

② il disegno
....

③ gli sport
....

④ la danza
....

⑤ gli hobby
....

Listen again and write the words.

la p ....

il d ....

gli s ....

la d ....

gli h ....

Listen again and write the words.

lo z ....

la z ....

la c ....

il f ....

la s ....

Listen, repeat, and copy.

① lo zio   ② la zia

....

③ la cugina

....

④ il fratello   ⑤ la sorella

....

Listen again and write the words.

il t ....

il c ....

la c ....

il g ....

la s ....

Listen, repeat, and copy.

① il tetto

....

② il capanno

....

③ la casa

....

④ il giardino

....

⑤ la staccionata

....

Day 5

What can you remember from this week?

1. Look at the pictures and circle the correct words.

① il tetto
il giardino

② il capanno
la staccionata

③ il giardino
la casa

④ il tetto
il capanno

⑤ la casa
la staccionata

2. Look at the pictures and write the letters in the correct order.

① il dgnoise

il d ....

② la dzana

la d ....

③ la ptuarit

la p ....

④ gli srtpo

gli s ....

⑤ gli hbyob

gli h ....

Week 14

3. Look at the pictures and write the correct words.

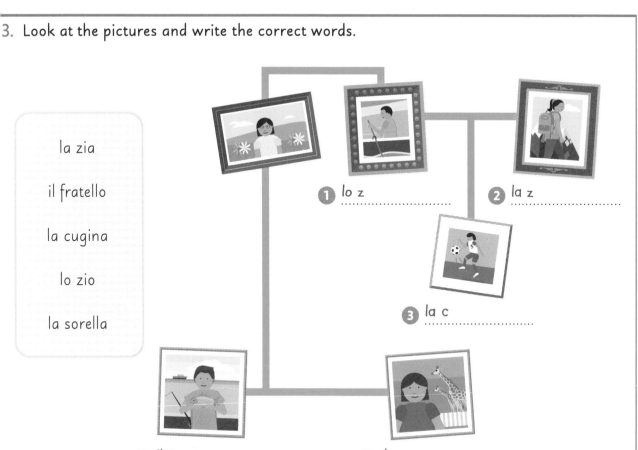

la zia

il fratello

la cugina

lo zio

la sorella

1 lo z ....

2 la z ....

3 la c ....

4 il f ....

5 la s ....

4. Match the pictures to the correct words.

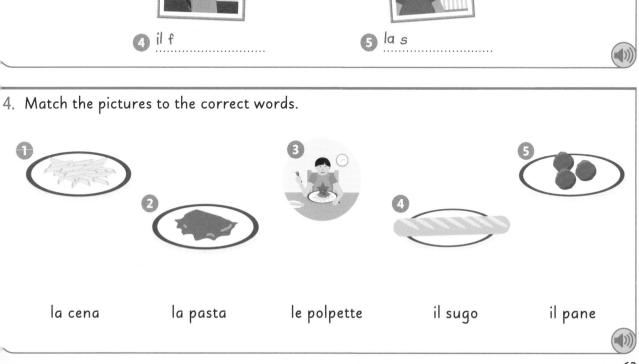

la cena   la pasta   le polpette   il sugo   il pane

63

Day 1

Listen, repeat, and copy.

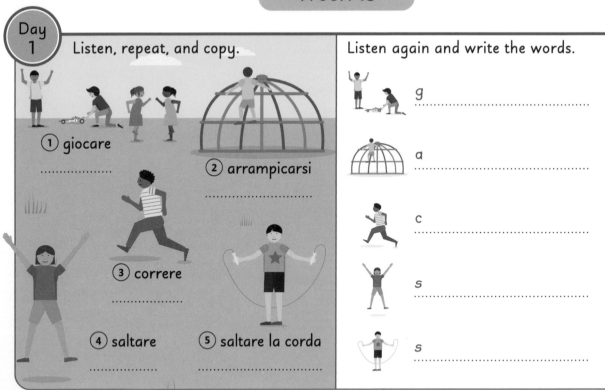

① giocare

② arrampicarsi

③ correre

④ saltare

⑤ saltare la corda

Listen again and write the words.

g ....

a ....

c ....

s ....

s ....

Day 2

Listen, repeat, and copy.

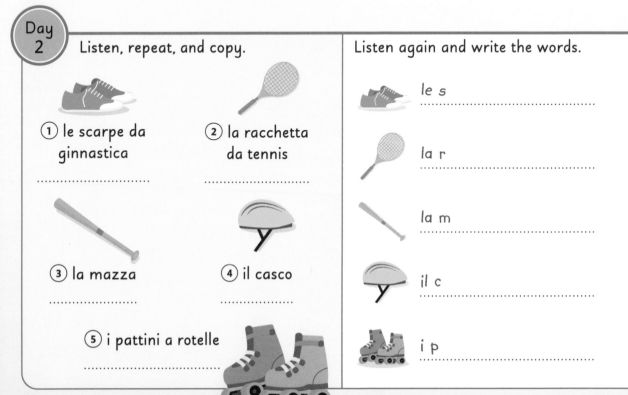

① le scarpe da ginnastica

② la racchetta da tennis

③ la mazza

④ il casco

⑤ i pattini a rotelle

Listen again and write the words.

le s ....

la r ....

la m ....

il c ....

i p ....

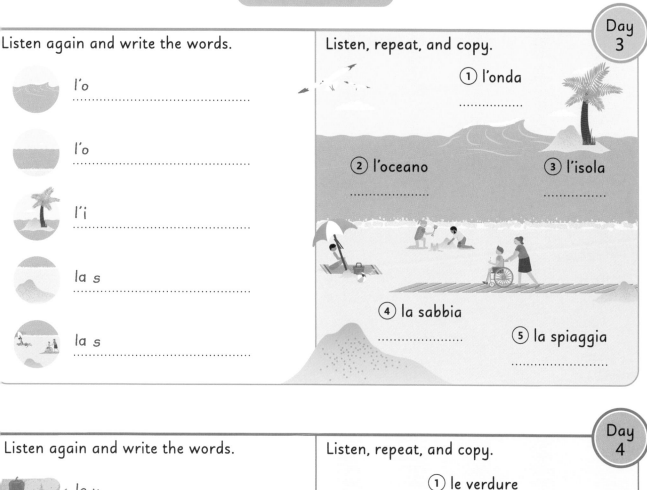

Day 3

Listen again and write the words.

l'o ....

l'o ....

l'i ....

la s ....

la s ....

Listen, repeat, and copy.

① l'onda ....

② l'oceano ....

③ l'isola ....

④ la sabbia ....

⑤ la spiaggia ....

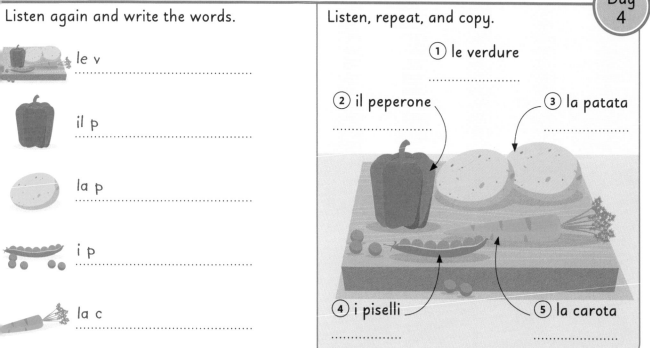

Day 4

Listen again and write the words.

le v ....

il p ....

la p ....

i p ....

la c ....

Listen, repeat, and copy.

① le verdure ....

② il peperone ....

③ la patata ....

④ i piselli ....

⑤ la carota ....

Day 5

What can you remember from this week?

1. Look at the pictures and mark the correct words.

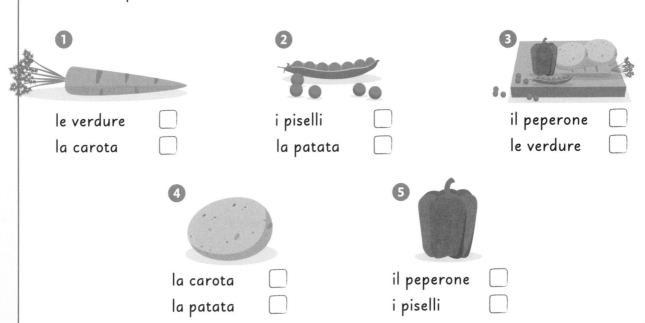

1

le verdure ☐
la carota ☐

2

i piselli ☐
la patata ☐

3

il peperone ☐
le verdure ☐

4

la carota ☐
la patata ☐

5

il peperone ☐
i piselli ☐

2. Look at the pictures and fill in the missing letters.

1 l' c _ a _ o

2  l' _ n _ a

3  _ a _ p _ a _ g _ a _

4 l _ _ s _ b _ i _

5  l' _ s _ l

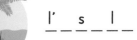

3. Match the pictures to the correct words.

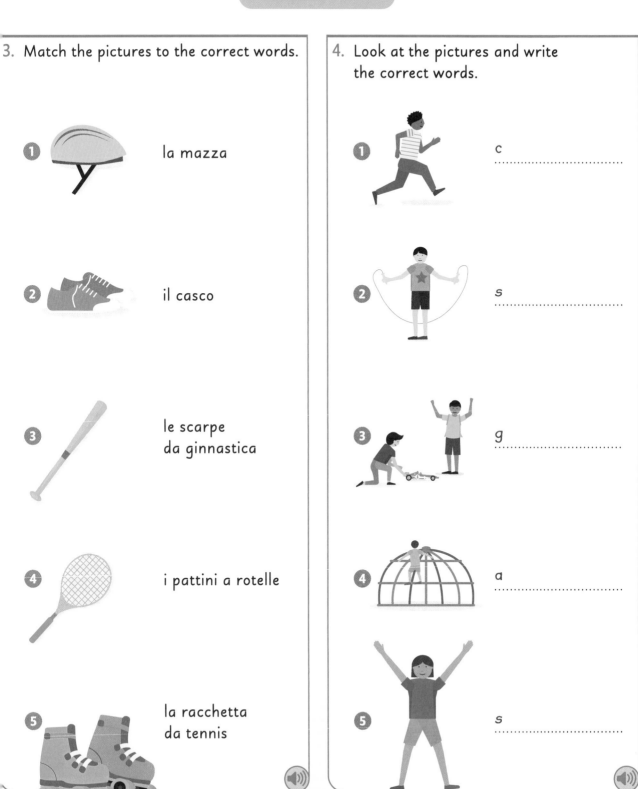

1 la mazza

2 il casco

3 le scarpe
da ginnastica

4 i pattini a rotelle

5 la racchetta
da tennis

4. Look at the pictures and write
the correct words.

1 c ....

2 s ....

3 g ....

4 a ....

5 s ....

Week 16

Day 1

Listen, repeat, and copy.

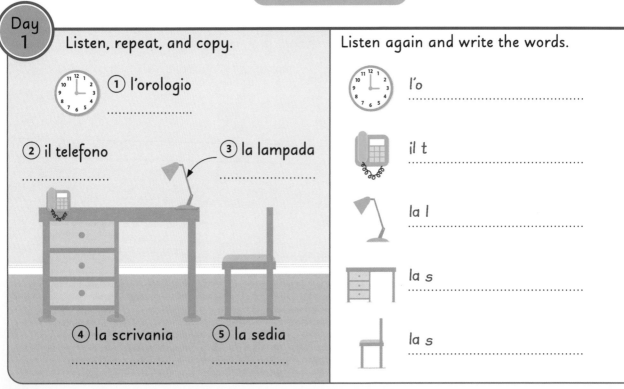

① l'orologio

....

② il telefono

....

③ la lampada

....

④ la scrivania

....

⑤ la sedia

....

Listen again and write the words.

l'o ....

il t ....

la l ....

la s ....

la s ....

Day 2

Listen, repeat, and copy.

① il cane

....

② il cucciolo

....

③ il gatto

....

④ il gattino

....

⑤ il topo

....

Listen again and write the words.

il c ....

il c ....

il g ....

il g ....

il t ....

Week 16

Listen again and write the words.

l ....

a ....

c ....

m ....

b ....

Listen, repeat, and copy.

① lavare
....

② asciugare
....

③ cucinare
....

④ mangiare
....

⑤ bere
....

Listen again and write the words.

la f ....

il p ....

il g ....

le c ....

l'i ....

Listen, repeat, and copy.

① la festa
....

② il palloncino
....

③ il gioco
....

④ le caramelle
....

⑤ l'invito
....

Week 16

Day 5 What can you remember from this week?

1. Look at the pictures and mark the correct words.

   1. le caramelle ☐
      il gioco ☐

   2. il palloncino ☐
      la festa ☐

   3. la festa ☐
      il gioco ☐

   4. l'invito ☐
      le caramelle ☐

   5. l'invito ☐
      il palloncino ☐

2. Look at the pictures and write the letters in the correct order.

   1. c n a e r u c i
      c ....

   2. m n r e g a i a
      m ....

   3. l v a e r a
      l ....

   4. a i e u s c r g a
      a ....

   5. b r e e
      b ....

3. Look at the pictures and write the correct words.

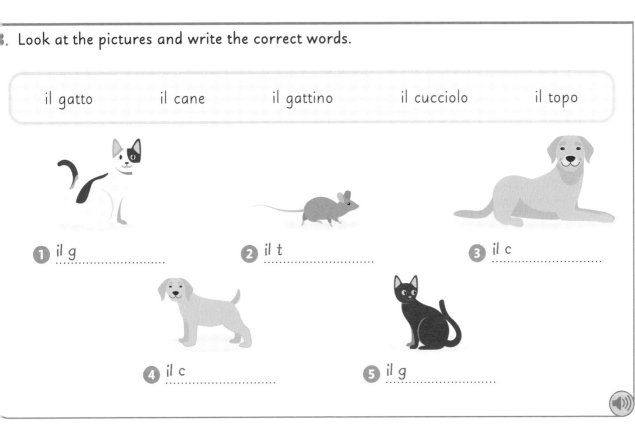

il gatto　　　　il cane　　　　il gattino　　　　il cucciolo　　　　il topo

1 il g ....

2 il t ....

3 il c ....

4 il c ....

5 il g ....

4. Look at the pictures and circle the correct words.

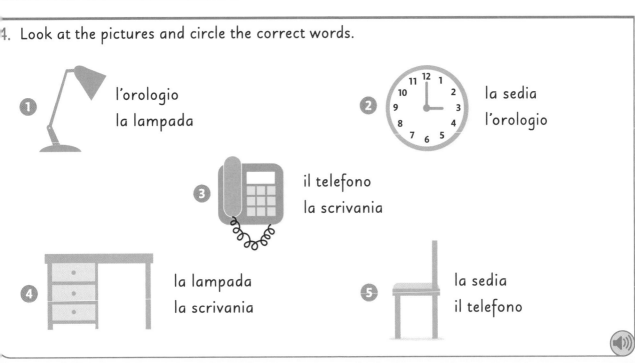

1 l'orologio
la lampada

2 la sedia
l'orologio

3 il telefono
la scrivania

4 la lampada
la scrivania

5 la sedia
il telefono

Week 17

Day 1

Listen, repeat, and copy.

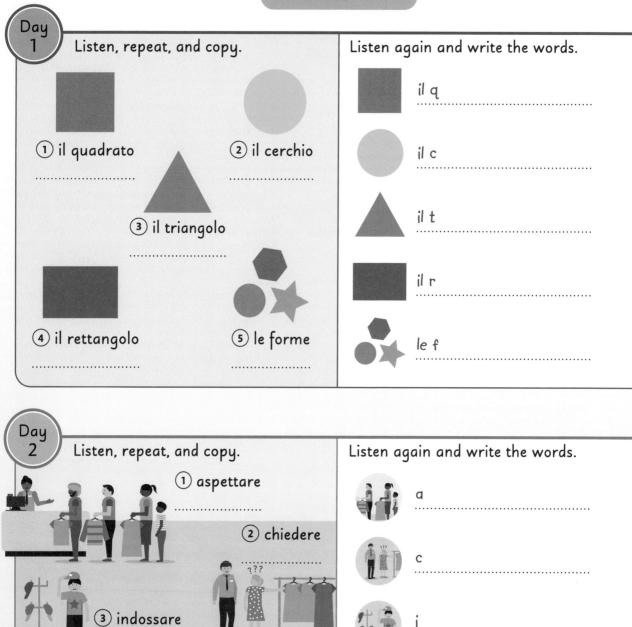

① il quadrato

② il cerchio

③ il triangolo

④ il rettangolo

⑤ le forme

Listen again and write the words.

il q ....

il c ....

il t ....

il r ....

le f ....

Day 2

Listen, repeat, and copy.

① aspettare

② chiedere

③ indossare

④ scegliere

⑤ fare spese

Listen again and write the words.

a ....

c ....

i ....

s ....

f ....

72

Listen again and write the words.

la l ....

il b ....

l'a ....

la c ....

la f ....

Listen, repeat, and copy.

① la libellula
....

② il bruco
....

③ l'ape
....

④ la coccinella
....

⑤ la formica
....

Listen again and write the words.

l'a ....

il s ....

la l ....

il f ....

le b ....

Listen, repeat, and copy.

① l'acqua
....

② il succo
....

③ la limonata
....

④ il frappè
....

⑤ le bibite
....

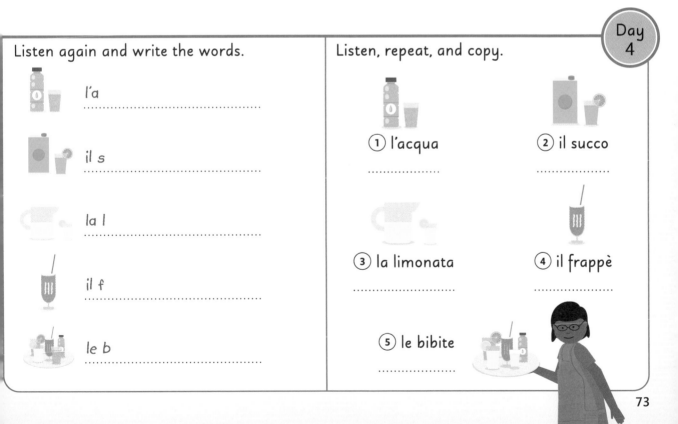

Week 17

Day 5   What can you remember from this week?

1. Match the pictures to the correct words.

1. aspettare

2. chiedere

3. fare spese

4. scegliere

5. indossare

2. Look at the pictures and mark the correct words.

1.
l'ape ☐
la coccinella ☐
la libellula ☐

2.
il bruco ☐
la formica ☐
l'ape ☐

3.
la formica ☐
la libellula ☐
la coccinella ☐

4.
il bruco ☐
l'ape ☐
la libellula ☐

5.
la coccinella ☐
il bruco ☐
la formica ☐

3. Look at the pictures and write the correct words.

l'acqua   il succo   le bibite   il frappè   la limonata

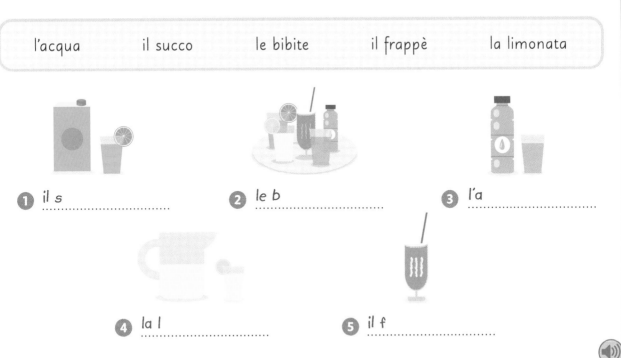

1 il s ....

2 le b ....

3 l'a ....

4 la l ....

5 il f ....

4. Look at the pictures and fill in the missing letters.

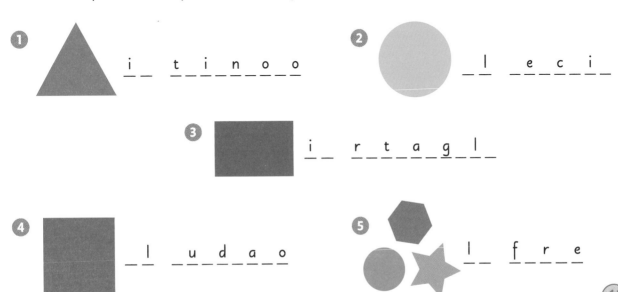

1 i _ t _ i _ n o o

2 _ l _ e _ c _ i _

3 i _ r _ t _ a g l _

4 _ l _ u d _ a _ o

5 l _ f _ r _ e

Day 1

Listen, repeat, and copy.

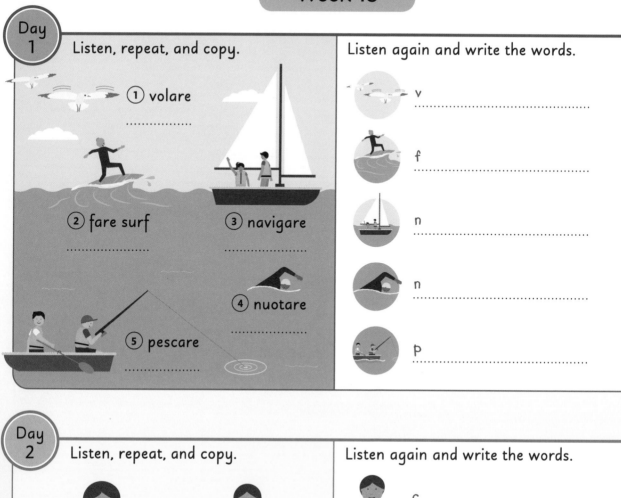

① volare

② fare surf

③ navigare

④ nuotare

⑤ pescare

Listen again and write the words.

v ....

f ....

n ....

n ....

p ....

Day 2

Listen, repeat, and copy.

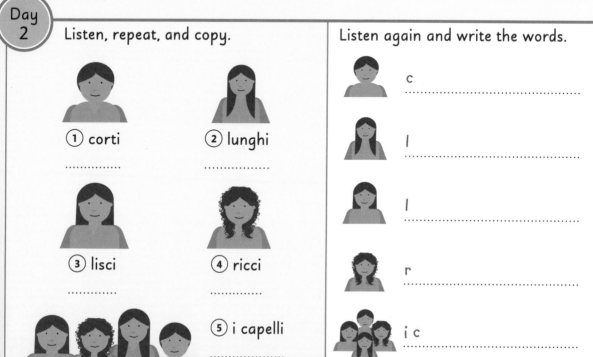

① corti

② lunghi

③ lisci

④ ricci

⑤ i capelli

Listen again and write the words.

c ....

l ....

l ....

r ....

i c ....

Listen again and write the words.

la v

....

il p

....

la d

....

l'i

....

l'a

....

Listen, repeat, and copy.

① la veterinaria

....

② il pompiere

....

③ la dottoressa

....

④ l'infermiere

....

⑤ l'agente di polizia

....

Listen again and write the words.

il g

....

il g

....

il b

....

gli a

....

l'a

....

Listen, repeat, and copy.

① il gruppo

....

② il genitore

....

③ il bambino

....

④ gli amici

....

⑤ l'adulto

....

Day 5

What can you remember from this week?

1. Read the words and mark the correct pictures.

1 la veterinaria

A ☐   B ☐

2 il pompiere

A ☐   B ☐

3 la dottoressa

A ☐   B ☐

4 l'agente di polizia

A ☐   B ☐

5 l'infermiere

A ☐   B ☐

2. Look at the picture and write the correct words.

lunghi

ricci

i capelli

corti

lisci

1 l c ....

2 c ....

3 l ....

4 l ....

5 r ....

3. Look at the pictures and write
the letters in the correct order.

1 f r e a   s r f u

f ....

2 p s c r e e a

p ....

3 v r l e o a

v ....

4 n t a o e u r

n ....

5 n g r e a a v i

n ....

4. Look at the pictures and circle
the correct words.

1 il genitore
il bambino

2 l'adulto
il gruppo

3 gli amici
il genitore

4 il bambino
il gruppo

5 gli amici
l'adulto

Day 1

Listen, repeat, and copy.

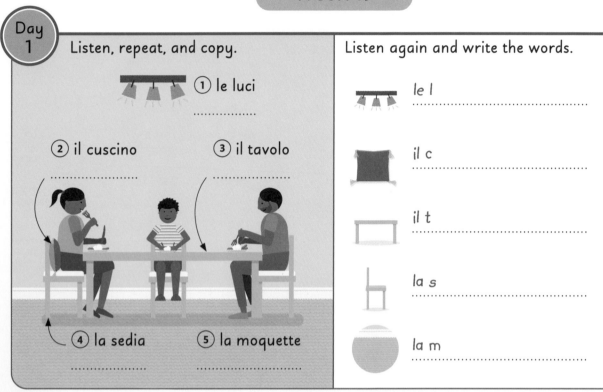

① le luci

② il cuscino

③ il tavolo

④ la sedia

⑤ la moquette

Listen again and write the words.

le l ......

il c ......

il t ......

la s ......

la m ......

Day 2

Listen, repeat, and copy.

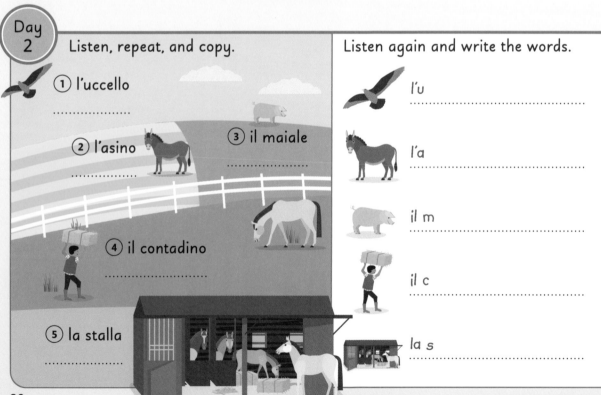

① l'uccello

② l'asino

③ il maiale

④ il contadino

⑤ la stalla

Listen again and write the words.

l'u ......

l'a ......

il m ......

il c ......

la s ......

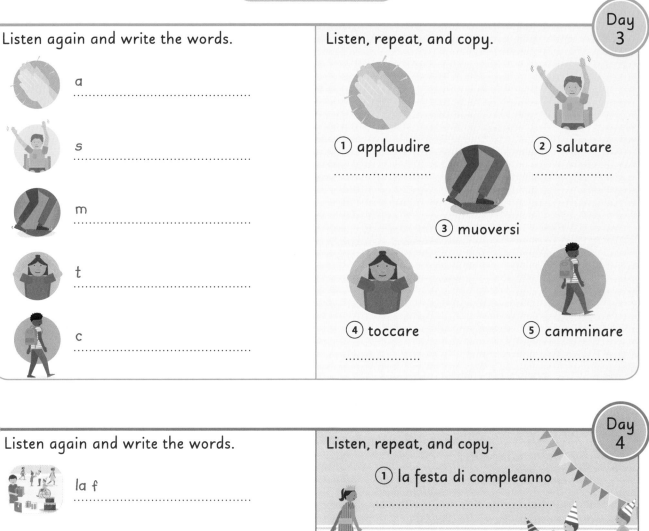

Day 3

Listen again and write the words.

a ....

s ....

m ....

t ....

c ....

Listen, repeat, and copy.

① applaudire
....

② salutare
....

③ muoversi
....

④ toccare
....

⑤ camminare
....

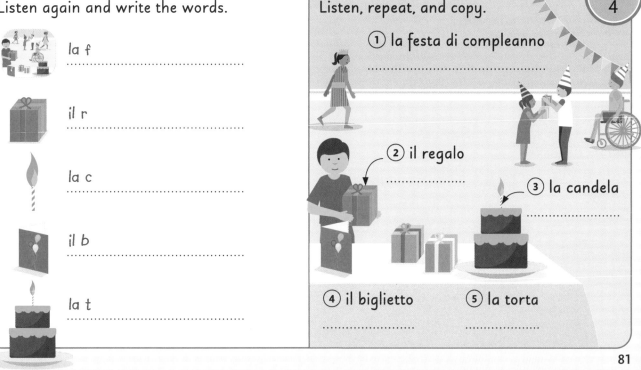

Day 4

Listen again and write the words.

la f ....

il r ....

la c ....

il b ....

la t ....

Listen, repeat, and copy.

① la festa di compleanno
....

② il regalo
....

③ la candela
....

④ il biglietto
....

⑤ la torta
....

Day 5

What can you remember from this week?

1. Match the pictures to the correct words.

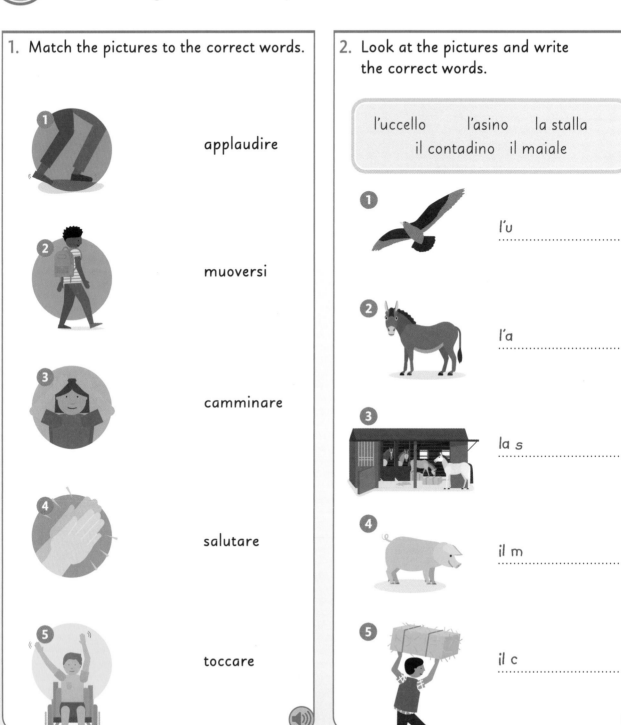

1. applaudire

2. muoversi

3. camminare

4. salutare

5. toccare

2. Look at the pictures and write the correct words.

l'uccello   l'asino   la stalla
il contadino   il maiale

1. l'u ....

2. l'a ....

3. la s ....

4. il m ....

5. il c ....

3. Look at the pictures and circle the correct words.

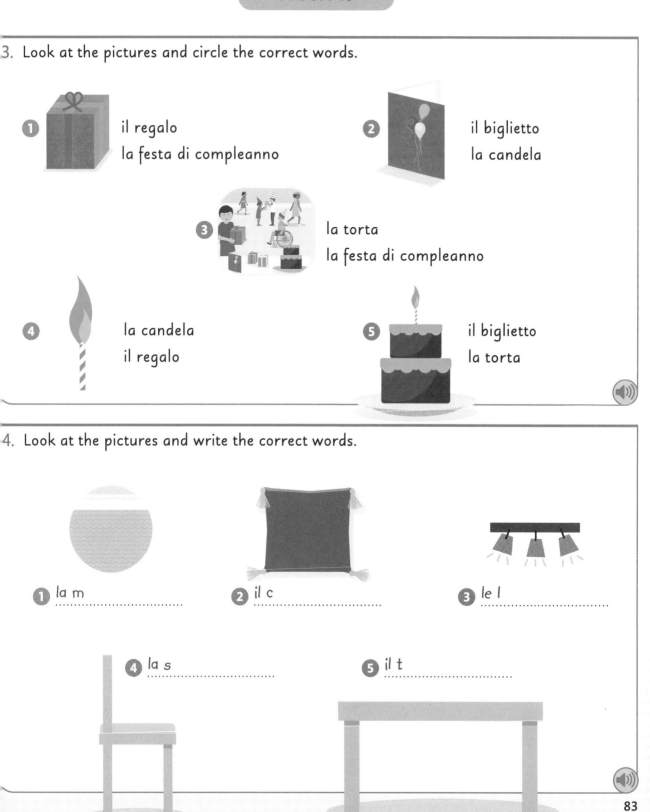

1   il regalo
la festa di compleanno

2   il biglietto
la candela

3   la torta
la festa di compleanno

4   la candela
il regalo

5   il biglietto
la torta

4. Look at the pictures and write the correct words.

1 la m ....

2 il c ....

3 le l ....

4 la s ....

5 il t ....

Week 20

Listen, repeat, and copy.

1 sciare
2 andare in bicicletta
3 segnare
4 pattinare sul ghiaccio
5 andare in skateboard

Listen again and write the words.

s ....
a ....
s ....
p ....
a ....

Day 2

Listen, repeat, and copy.

1 il delfino
2 la balena
3 lo squalo
4 la medusa
5 il polpo

Listen again and write the words.

il d ....
la b ....
lo s ....
la m ....
il p ....

Listen again and write the words.

la s ....

la m ....

il p ....

il g ....

le d ....

Listen, repeat, and copy.

① la spalla ....

② la mano ....

③ il petto ....

④ il gomito ....

⑤ le dita della mano ....

Listen again and write the words.

la p ....

la f ....

la c ....

il l ....

il l ....

Listen, repeat, and copy.

① la pesca ....

② la fragola ....

③ la ciliegia ....

④ il limone ....

⑤ il lime ....

Day 5

What can you remember from this week?

1. Read the words and mark the correct pictures.

① segnare

A ☐   B ☐

② pattinare sul ghiaccio

A ☐   B ☐

③ sciare

A ☐   B ☐

④ andare in bicicletta

A ☐   B ☐

⑤ andare in skateboard

A ☐   B ☐

2. Look at the pictures and fill in the missing letters.

① i _ d _ l _ i _ o

② i _ m d s _

③ i _ p _ l _ o

④ _l _ s u l _

⑤ _l _ b _ l n _

3. Match the pictures to the correct words.

la spalla

la mano

le dita
della mano

il petto

il gomito

4. Look at the pictures and write
the correct words.

il lime   la ciliegia   la pesca
il limone   la fragola

1 il l ....

2 la c ....

3 la f ....

4 la p ....

5 il l ....

Day 1

Listen, repeat, and copy.

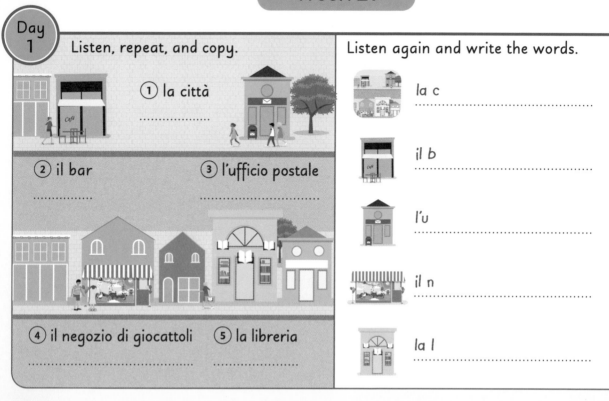

① la città

② il bar ③ l'ufficio postale

④ il negozio di giocattoli ⑤ la libreria

Listen again and write the words.

la c ....

il b ....

l'u ....

il n ....

la l ....

Day 2

Listen, repeat, and copy.

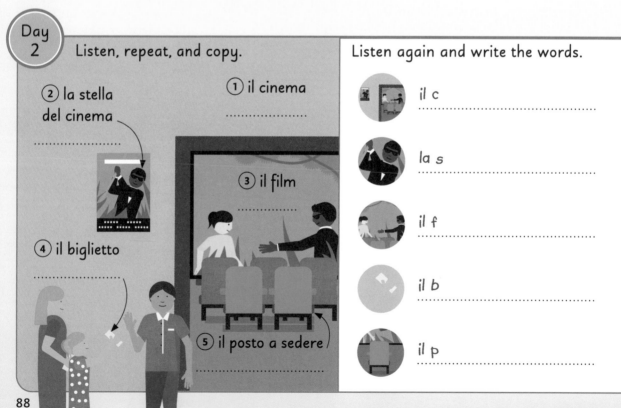

② la stella del cinema

① il cinema

③ il film

④ il biglietto

⑤ il posto a sedere

Listen again and write the words.

il c ....

la s ....

il f ....

il b ....

il p ....

Listen again and write the words.

il t ....

l'e-m ....

l'e-b ....

il m ....

le a ....

Listen, repeat, and copy.

① il tablet ....

② l'e-mail ....

③ l'e-book ....

④ il messaggio ....

⑤ le applicazioni ....

Listen again and write the words.

l'a ....

l'a ....

lo s ....

la p ....

la b ....

Listen, repeat, and copy.

① l'altalena ....

② l'altalena carosello ....

③ lo scivolo ....

④ la panchina ....

⑤ la bicicletta ....

Day 5

What can you remember from this week?

---

1. Look at the pictures and write the correct words.

1. il t ....

2. l'e-b ....

3. il m ....

4. le a ....

5. l'e-m ....

---

2. Match the pictures to the correct words.

1. l'ufficio postale

2. il bar

3. la libreria

4. la città

5. il negozio di giocattoli

3. Look at the pictures and circle the correct words.

il posto a sedere
il cinema

il film
il cinema

la stella del cinema
il posto a sedere

il biglietto
la stella del cinema

il biglietto
il film

4. Read the words and mark the correct pictures.

1 la bicicletta

A ☐   B ☐

2 l'altalena

A ☐   B ☐

3 la panchina

A ☐   B ☐

4 l'altalena carosello

A ☐   B ☐

5 lo scivolo

A ☐   B ☐

Day 1

Listen, repeat, and copy.

① la data ② la domanda
....

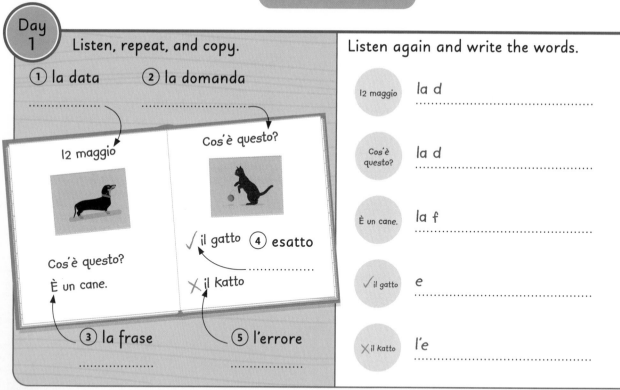

l2 maggio

Cos'è questo?

Cos'è questo?

È un cane.

✓ il gatto ④ esatto
....

✗ il katto

③ la frase ⑤ l'errore
....

Listen again and write the words.

l2 maggio — la d ....

Cos'è questo? — la d ....

È un cane. — la f ....

✓ il gatto — e ....

✗ il katto — l'e ....

Day 2

Listen, repeat, and copy.

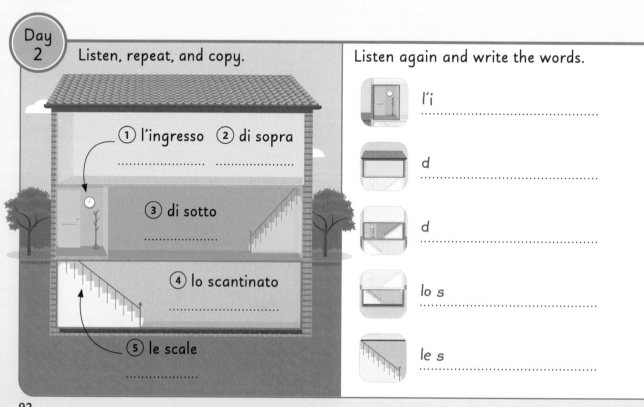

① l'ingresso ② di sopra
....

③ di sotto
....

④ lo scantinato
....

⑤ le scale
....

Listen again and write the words.

l'i ....

d ....

d ....

lo s ....

le s ....

Listen again and write the words.

p ....

r ....

f ....

m ....

e ....

Listen, repeat, and copy.

① pulire
....

② rilassarsi
....

③ fare i compiti
....

④ mettere
in ordine
....

⑤ esercitarsi
....

Listen again and write the words.

la p ....

il n ....

gli o ....

l'a ....

il c ....

Listen, repeat, and copy.

① la piscina
....

② il nuoto
....

③ gli occhialini
....

④ l'asciugamano
....

⑤ il costume da bagno
....

Day 5

What can you remember from this week?

1. Look at the picture and write the correct words.

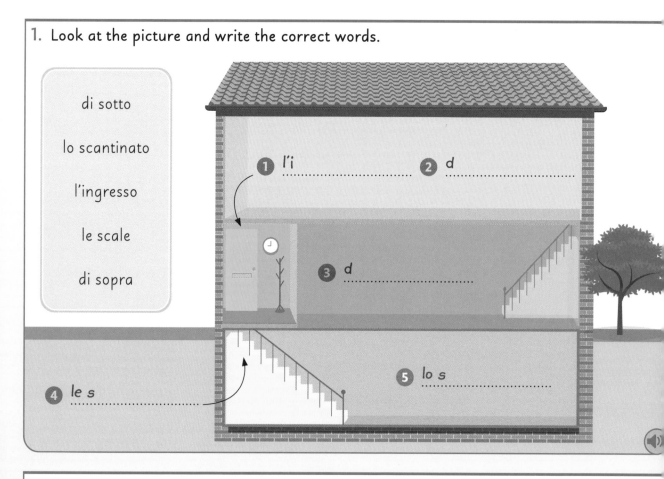

di sotto

lo scantinato

l'ingresso

le scale

di sopra

1 l'i ....

2 d ....

3 d ....

4 le s ....

5 lo s ....

2. Match the pictures to the correct words.

mettere in ordine   rilassarsi   fare i compiti   pulire   esercitarsi

3. Look at the pictures and circle the correct words.

1. la piscina
   l'asciugamano

2. gli occhialini
   la piscina

3. il costume da bagno
   l'asciugamano

4. gli occhialini
   il nuoto

5. il nuoto
   il costume da bagno

4. Look at the pictures and fill in the missing letters.

1. ✓ il gatto   _ e _ a _ t _

2. Cos'è questo?   _ l _ _ d _ m _ n _ a

3. 12 maggio   _ a _ _ a _ a

4. ✗ il katto   l' _ r _ o _ e

5. È un cane.   _ a _ _ r _ s _

Day 1

Listen, repeat, and copy.

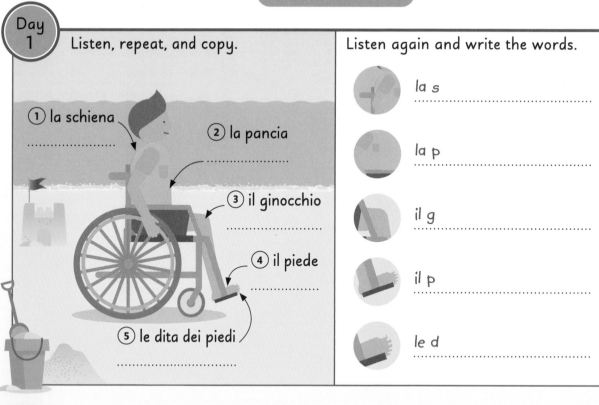

① la schiena
....

② la pancia
....

③ il ginocchio
....

④ il piede
....

⑤ le dita dei piedi
....

Listen again and write the words.

la s ....

la p ....

il g ....

il p ....

le d ....

Day 2

Listen, repeat, and copy.

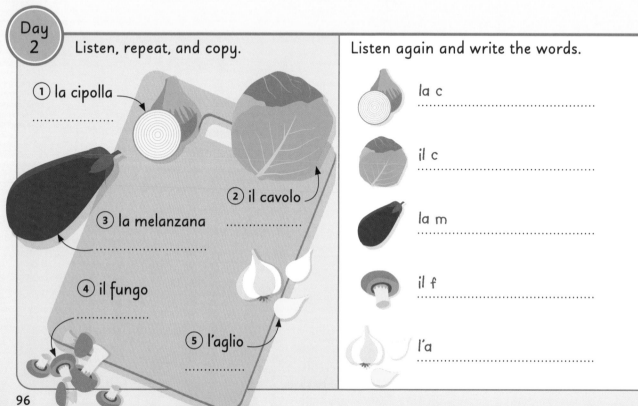

① la cipolla
....

② il cavolo

③ la melanzana ....
....

④ il fungo
....

⑤ l'aglio
....

Listen again and write the words.

la c ....

il c ....

la m ....

il f ....

l'a ....

Listen again and write the words.

 il g ....

 la p ....

 il p ....

 il c ....

 la g ....

Listen, repeat, and copy.

① il golf
....

② la pallavolo
....

③ il ping pong
....

④ il calcio
....

 ⑤ la ginnastica artistica

....

Listen again and write the words.

 la c ....

 la c ....

 il f ....

 la l ....

 la t ....

Listen, repeat, and copy.

① la cascata
....

② la caverna
....

③ il fiume
....

④ la lucertola
....

 ⑤ la tartaruga
....

Day 5 What can you remember from this week?

1. Look at the pictures and mark the correct words.

1. la cipolla ☐
   il cavolo ☐

2. il fungo ☐
   l'aglio ☐

3. il cavolo ☐
   la melanzana ☐

4. la cipolla ☐
   il fungo ☐

5. l'aglio ☐
   la melanzana ☐

2. Look at the pictures and write the correct words.

1. il f ....

2. la c ....

3. la c ....

4. la l ....

5. la t ....

3. Look at the pictures and circle the correct words.

 il golf / la ginnastica artistica

 la pallavolo / il calcio

 il ping pong / la ginnastica artistica

 la pallavolo / il ping pong

 il calcio / il golf

4. Look at the picture and write the correct words.

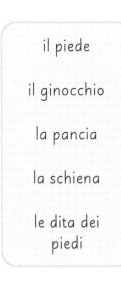

il piede

il ginocchio

la pancia

la schiena

le dita dei piedi

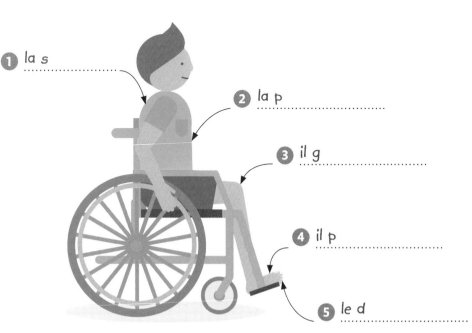

1 la s ....

2 la p ....

3 il g ....

4 il p ....

5 le d ....

Week 24

Day 1

Listen, repeat, and copy.

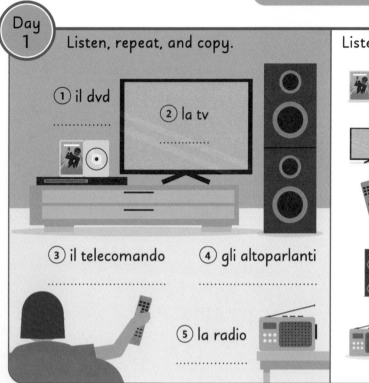

① il dvd

② la tv

③ il telecomando

④ gli altoparlanti

⑤ la radio

Listen again and write the words.

 il d ....

 la t ....

 il t ....

 gli a ....

 la r ....

Day 2

Listen, repeat, and copy.

① telefonare

② mandare un'e-mail

③ inviare

④ parlare

⑤ gridare

Listen again and write the words.

 t ....

 m ....

 i ....

 p ....

 g ....

Listen again and write the words.

il d ....

la p ....

il c ....

il c ....

il s ....

Listen, repeat, and copy.

① il deserto
....

② la piramide
....

③ il cammello
....

④ il coccodrillo
....

⑤ il serpente
....

Listen again and write the words.

la s ....

l'a ....

l'a ....

il p ....

il t ....

Listen, repeat, and copy.

① la stazione degli autobus
....

② l'autobus
....

③ l'autista
....

④ il passeggero
....

⑤ il taxi
....

Week 24

Day 5 What can you remember from this week?

1. Read the words and mark the correct pictures.

1 la radio

A ☐   B ☐

2 la tv

A ☐   B ☐

3 il dvd

A ☐   B ☐

4 il telecomando

A ☐   B ☐

5 gli altoparlanti

A ☐   B ☐

2. Look at the pictures and write the correct words.

1 il c ....

2 la p ....

3 il d ....

4 il s ....

5 il c ....

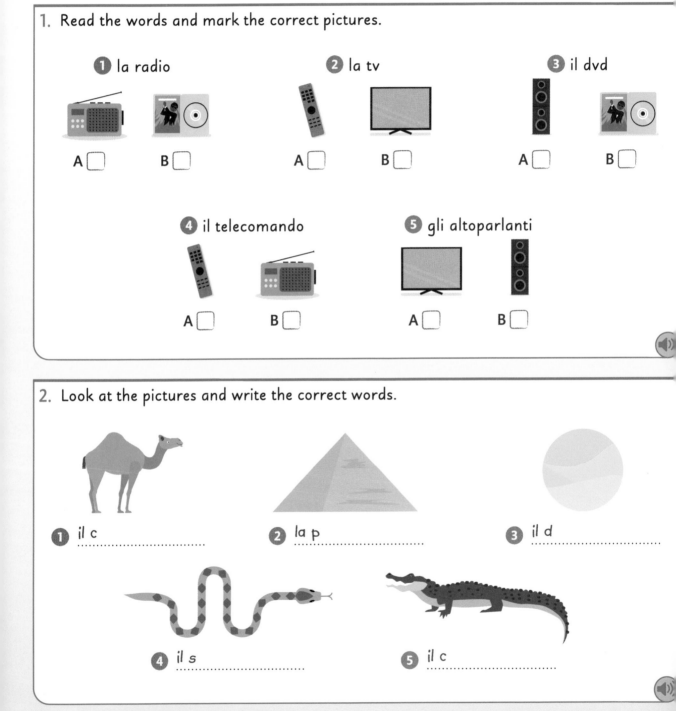

3. Match the pictures to the correct words.

il passeggero

il taxi

la stazione
degli autobus

l'autobus

l'autista

4. Look at the pictures and circle the correct words.

inviare

telefonare

mandare un'e-mail

gridare

parlare

inviare

telefonare

gridare

parlare

mandare un'e-mail

Day 1

Listen, repeat, and copy.

Listen again and write the words.

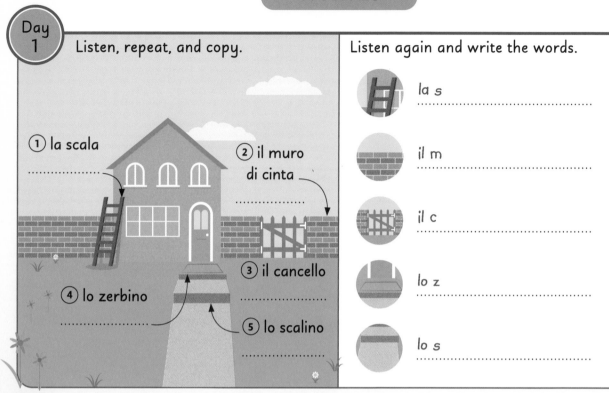

① la scala

② il muro di cinta

③ il cancello

④ lo zerbino

⑤ lo scalino

la s ....

il m ....

il c ....

lo z ....

lo s ....

Day 2

Listen, repeat, and copy.

Listen again and write the words.

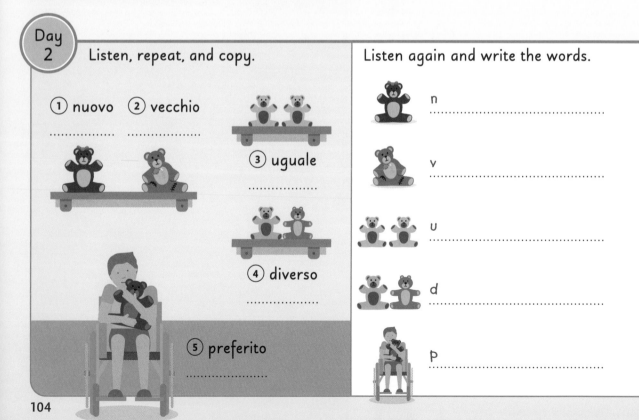

① nuovo ② vecchio

③ uguale

④ diverso

⑤ preferito

n ....

v ....

u ....

d ....

p ....

Listen again and write the words.

l'a
....

il c
....

la m
....

il c
....

l'a
....

Listen, repeat, and copy.

① l'ambulanza
....

② il camion

③ la moto
....

④ il camion dei pompieri
....

⑤ l'auto
....

Listen again and write the words.

s
....

s
....

f
....

l
....

v
....

Listen, repeat, and copy.

① sognare
....

② svegliarsi
....

③ fare il letto
....

④ lavarsi i denti
....

⑤ vestirsi
....

What can you remember from this week?

1. Look at the pictures and write the correct words.

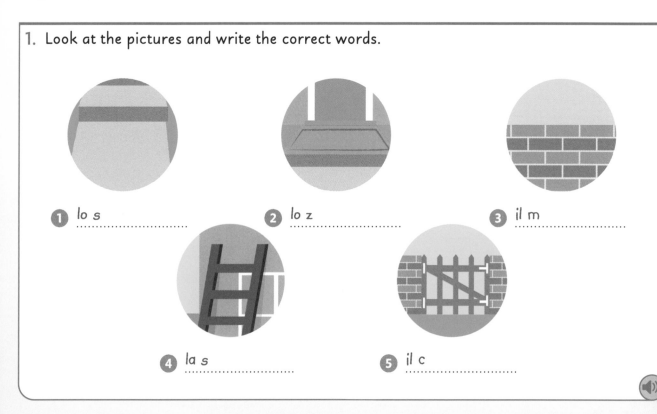

① lo s ....

② lo z ....

③ il m ....

④ la s ....

⑤ il c ....

2. Match the pictures to the correct words.

① ② ③ ④ ⑤

il camion   l'auto   l'ambulanza   la moto   il camion dei pompieri

3. Read the words and mark the correct pictures.

① svegliarsi   A ☐   B ☐

② fare il letto   A ☐   B ☐

③ lavarsi i denti   A ☐   B ☐

④ vestirsi   A ☐   B ☐

⑤ sognare   A ☐   B ☐

4. Look at the pictures and fill in the missing letters.

①    u _ u _ l _

②    d _ v _ r _ o

③    n _ o _ o

④    p _ e _ e _ i _ o

⑤    v _ c _ h _ o

Week 26

Day 1

Listen, repeat, and copy.

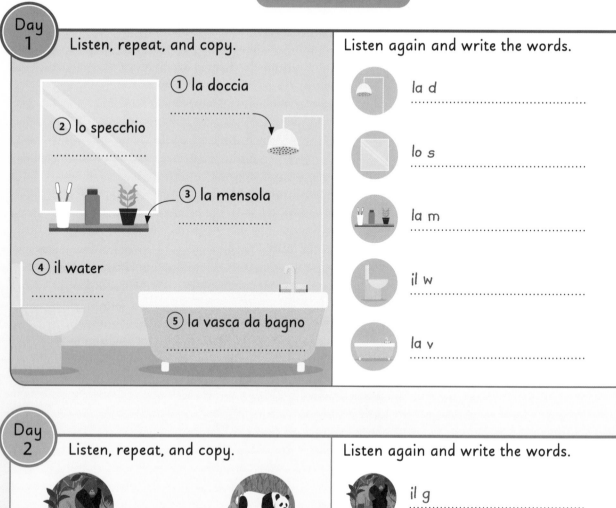

① la doccia

② lo specchio

③ la mensola

④ il water

⑤ la vasca da bagno

Listen again and write the words.

la d ....

lo s ....

la m ....

il w ....

la v ....

Day 2

Listen, repeat, and copy.

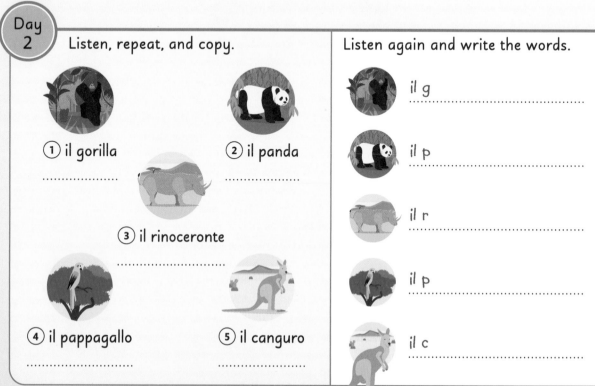

① il gorilla

② il panda

③ il rinoceronte

④ il pappagallo

⑤ il canguro

Listen again and write the words.

il g ....

il p ....

il r ....

il p ....

il c ....

Day 3

Listen again and write the words.

c ....

f ....

p ....

a ....

r ....

Listen, repeat, and copy.

① cadere
....

② farsi male
....

③ piangere
....

④ aiutare
....

⑤ raccontare
....

Day 4

Listen again and write the words.

la s ....

il g ....

il m ....

i g ....

gli s ....

Listen, repeat, and copy.

① la sciarpa
....

② il giubbotto
....

③ il maglione
....

④ i guanti
....

⑤ gli stivali
....

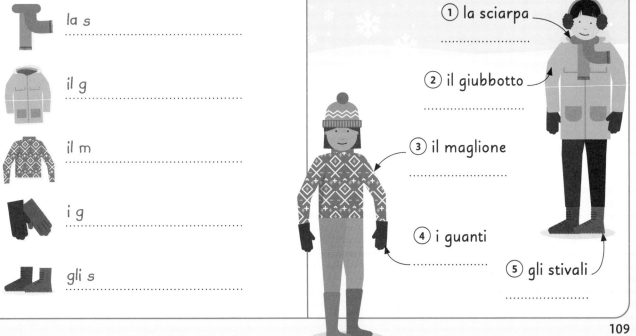

Day 5

What can you remember from this week?

1. Look at the pictures and write the correct words.

1. r ....

2. p ....

3. a ....

4. f ....

5. c ....

2. Look at the pictures and mark the correct words.

1.
il rinoceronte ☐
il canguro ☐
il pappagallo ☐

2.
il gorilla ☐
il panda ☐
il rinoceronte ☐

3.
il pappagallo ☐
il rinoceronte ☐
il gorilla ☐

4.
il canguro ☐
il gorilla ☐
il panda ☐

5.
il panda ☐
il pappagallo ☐
il canguro ☐

3. Look at the pictures and write the correct words.

il giubbotto   gli stivali   i guanti   la sciarpa   il maglione

1 gli s ....

2 il m ....

3 la s ....

4 il g ....

5 i g ....

4. Look at the pictures and circle the correct words.

1 la doccia
la vasca da bagno

2 il water
la mensola

3 la vasca da bagno
lo specchio

4 lo specchio
la mensola

5 la doccia
il water

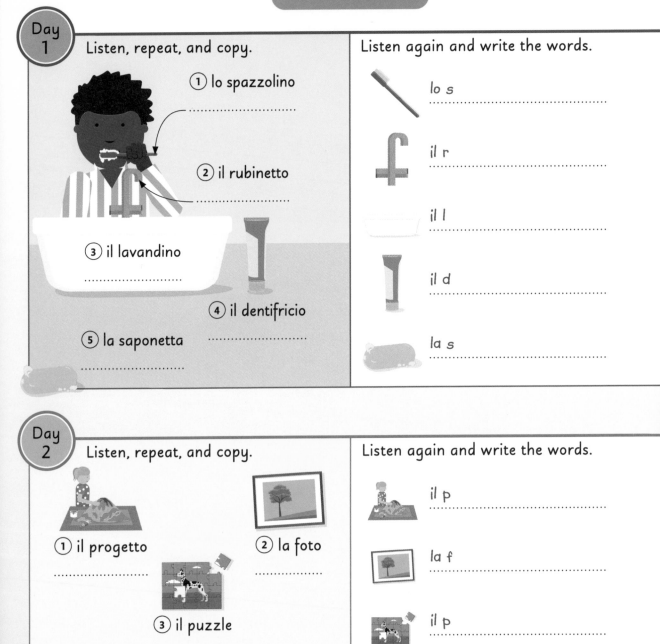

Day 1

Listen, repeat, and copy.

1. lo spazzolino
2. il rubinetto
3. il lavandino
4. il dentifricio
5. la saponetta

Listen again and write the words.

lo s

il r

il l

il d

la s

Day 2

Listen, repeat, and copy.

1. il progetto
2. la foto
3. il puzzle
4. la storia
5. la lezione

Aa Bb Cc

Listen again and write the words.

il p

la f

il p

la s

la l

Listen again and write the words.

s ....

e ....

a ....

a ....

a ....

Listen, repeat, and copy.

① spaventato
....

② emozionata
....

③ amichevole
....

④ assetato
....

⑤ affamato
....

Listen again and write the words.

la m ....

il l ....

il c ....

la f ....

la b ....

Listen, repeat, and copy.

① la montagna
....

② il lago
....

③ il castello
....

④ la foresta
....

⑤ la barca
....

113

Day 5

What can you remember from this week?

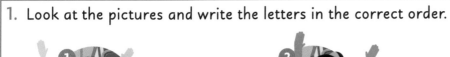

1. Look at the pictures and write the letters in the correct order.

(s v p t a a e n t o)

s _ _ _ _ _ _ _ _ _

(e z i a t m n a o o)

e _ _ _ _ _ _ _ _ _

(a h e v i c m o l e)

a _ _ _ _ _ _ _ _ _

(a t s s e t o a)

a _ _ _ _ _ _ _

(a m a t f a o f)

a _ _ _ _ _ _ _

2. Match the pictures to the correct words.

il dentifricio   la saponetta   il lavandino   il rubinetto   lo spazzolino

3. Look at the pictures and mark the correct words.

il progetto ☐
la foto ☐

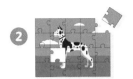

la storia ☐
il puzzle ☐

la lezione ☐
la foto ☐

la storia ☐
il progetto ☐

il puzzle ☐
la lezione ☐

4. Look at the pictures and fill in the missing letters.

1

l _ f _ r _ s _ a

2

_ a _ o _ t _ g _ a

3

i _ c _ s _ e _ l _

4

_ l _ a _ o

5

l _ b _ r _ a

Day 1

Listen, repeat, and copy.

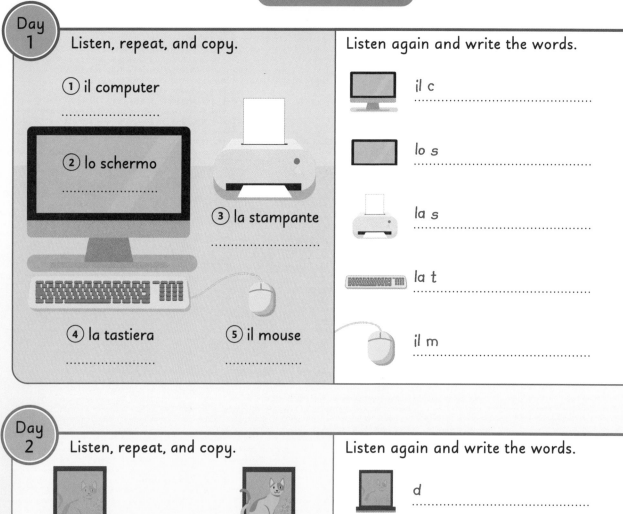

① il computer

....

② lo schermo

....

③ la stampante

....

④ la tastiera

....

⑤ il mouse

....

Listen again and write the words.

il c ....

lo s ....

la s ....

la t ....

il m ....

Day 2

Listen, repeat, and copy.

① dentro

....

② fuori

....

③ tra

....

④ sopra

....

⑤ sotto

....

Listen again and write the words.

d ....

f ....

t ....

s ....

s ....

Week 28

Listen again and write the words.

il t ....

n ....

n ....

s ....

v ....

Listen, repeat, and copy.

① il tempo   ② nebbioso
....

③ nuvoloso   ④ soleggiato
....

                ⑤ ventoso
                ....

Listen again and write the words.

il l ....

il c ....

la r ....

il g ....

il p ....

Listen, repeat, and copy.

① il luna park
....

② il circo   ③ la ruota panoramica
....

④ il gelato   ⑤ il pagliaccio
....

Day 5 What can you remember from this week?

1. Read the words and mark the correct pictures.

1 dentro   A ☐   B ☐

2 fuori   A ☐   B ☐

3 tra   A ☐   B ☐

4 sopra   A ☐   B ☐

5 sotto   A ☐   B ☐

2. Look at the pictures and write the correct words.

1 n ....

2 s ....

3 il t ....

4 v ....

5 n ....

3. Look at the pictures and circle the correct words.

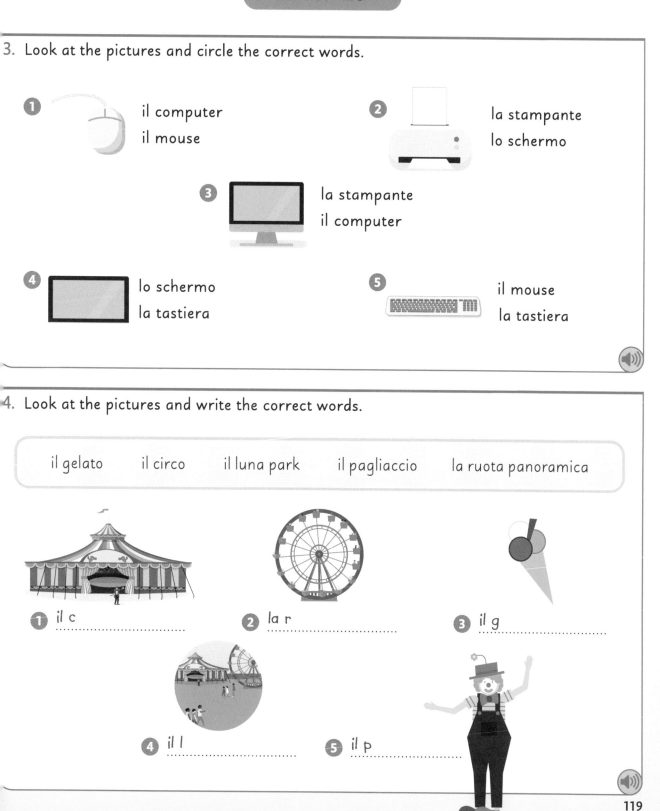

❶ il computer
il mouse

❷ la stampante
lo schermo

❸ la stampante
il computer

❹ lo schermo
la tastiera

❺ il mouse
la tastiera

4. Look at the pictures and write the correct words.

il gelato   il circo   il luna park   il pagliaccio   la ruota panoramica

❶ il c ....

❷ la r ....

❸ il g ....

❹ il l ....

❺ il p ....

Day 1

Listen, repeat, and copy.

① la zuppa   ② la torta

③ il riso   ④ i fagioli

⑤ la carne

Listen again and write the words.

la z ....

la t ....

il r ....

i f ....

la c ....

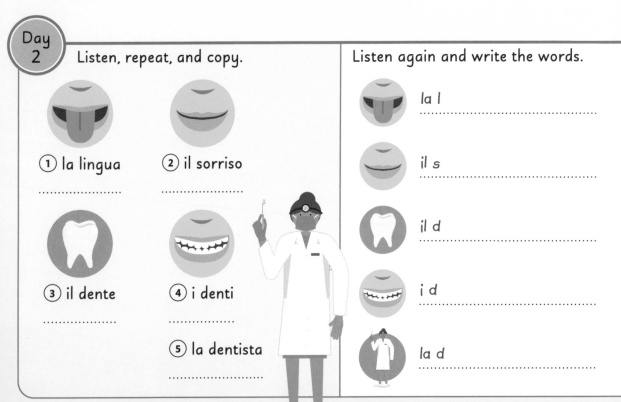

Day 2

Listen, repeat, and copy.

① la lingua   ② il sorriso

③ il dente   ④ i denti

⑤ la dentista

Listen again and write the words.

la l ....

il s ....

il d ....

i d ....

la d ....

Listen again and write the words.

c ....

t ....

p ....

u ....

c ....

Listen, repeat, and copy.

1 cercare ....

2 trovare ....

3 provare ....

4 unire ....

5 completare ....

Listen again and write the words.

la p ....

il s ....

la c ....

il p ....

la r ....

Listen, repeat, and copy.

1 la pesca ....

2 il salvagente ....

3 la canna da pesca ....

4 il pesce ....

5 la rete ....

Day 5

What can you remember from this week?

---

1. Look at the pictures and fill in the missing letters.

   c _ r a _ e

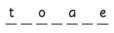   t _ o _ a _ e

   u _ i _ e

   c _ m _ l _ t _ r _

   _ r _ v _ r _

---

2. Match the pictures to the correct words.

 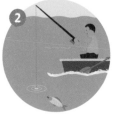   

la pesca   il pesce   il salvagente   la canna da pesca   la rete

3. Look at the pictures and write the correct words.

1. i d ....

2. la l ....

3. il d ....

4. il s ....

5. la d ....

4. Look at the pictures and mark the correct words.

1.
   la zuppa ☐
   i fagioli ☐
   il riso ☐

2.
   la carne ☐
   la torta ☐
   i fagioli ☐

3.
   il riso ☐
   la zuppa ☐
   la torta ☐

4.
   i fagioli ☐
   la carne ☐
   la zuppa ☐

5.
   la torta ☐
   il riso ☐
   la carne ☐

Day 1

Listen, repeat, and copy.

Listen again and write the words.

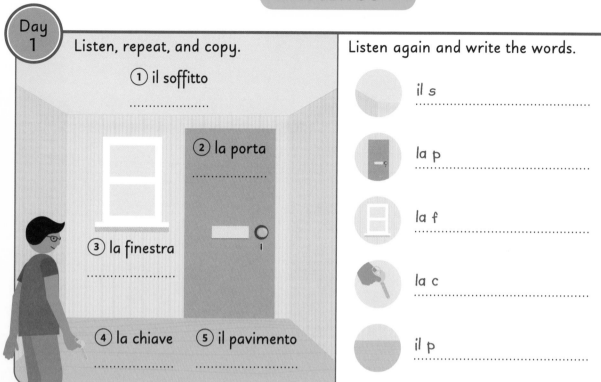

① il soffitto

....

② la porta

....

③ la finestra

....

④ la chiave   ⑤ il pavimento

....

il s ....

la p ....

la f ....

la c ....

il p ....

Day 2

Listen, repeat, and copy.

Listen again and write the words.

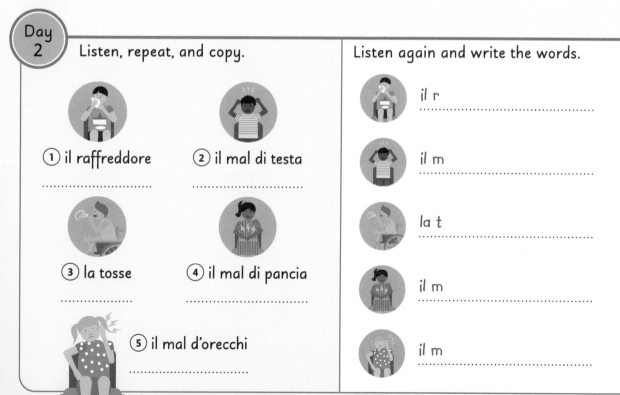

① il raffreddore   ② il mal di testa

....

③ la tosse   ④ il mal di pancia

....

⑤ il mal d'orecchi

....

il r ....

il m ....

la t ....

il m ....

il m ....

Day 3

Listen again and write the words.

la l ....

il f ....

la b ....

il n ....

l'i ....

Listen, repeat, and copy.

① la lettera ....

② il francobollo ....

③ la busta ....

④ il nome ....

Sofia

Via Roma 10
20121 Milano

⑤ l'indirizzo ....

Day 4

Listen again and write the words.

la c ....

le c ....

il p ....

il b ....

il m ....

Listen, repeat, and copy.

① la campagna ....

② le colline ....

③ il paese ....

④ il bosco ....

⑤ il mercato ....

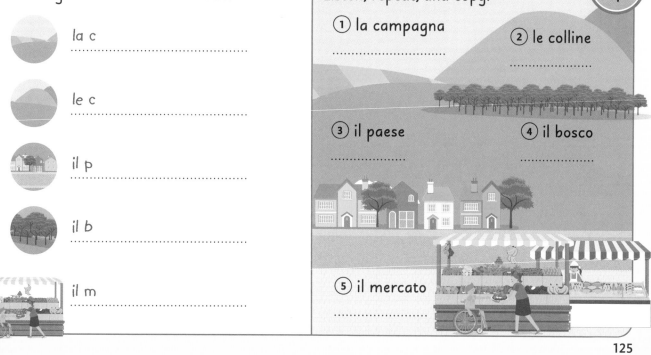

Day 5

What can you remember from this week?

1. Look at the pictures and write the correct words.

le colline   il paese   il bosco
la campagna   il mercato

1 il p ....

2 le c ....

3 la c ....

4 il b ....

5 il m ....

2. Look at the pictures and mark the correct words.

1 la lettera ☐
il francobollo ☐

2 Via Roma 10
20121 Milano
il nome ☐
l'indirizzo ☐

3 la busta ☐
la lettera ☐

4 l'indirizzo ☐
il francobollo ☐

5 Sofia
la busta ☐
il nome ☐

3. Read the words and mark the correct pictures.

1 il raffreddore

A ☐   B ☐

2 il mal di testa

A ☐   B ☐

3 la tosse

A ☐   B ☐

4 il mal d'orecchi

A ☐   B ☐

5 il mal di pancia

A ☐   B ☐

4. Look at the pictures and write the correct words.

1 il s ....

2 la f ....

3 la p ....

4 il p ....

5 la c ....

Week 31

Day 1

Listen, repeat, and copy.

① il sito web   ② il caricabatterie

③ il computer

④ le cuffie   ⑤ il cellulare

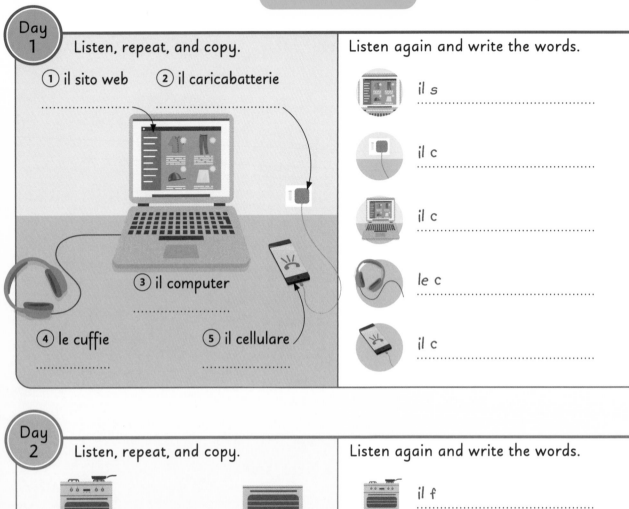

Listen again and write the words.

il s ....

il c ....

il c ....

le c ....

il c ....

Day 2

Listen, repeat, and copy.

① il fornello   ② il forno

③ il cestino

④ la credenza   ⑤ il frigorifero

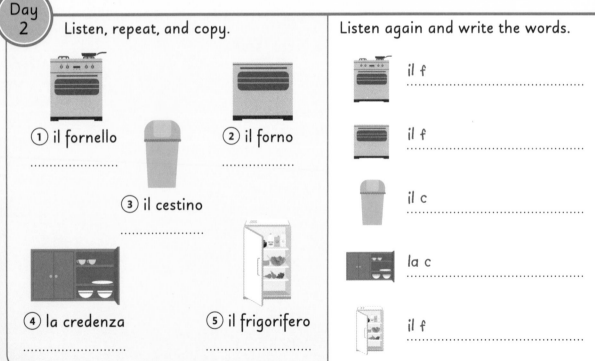

Listen again and write the words.

il f ....

il f ....

il c ....

la c ....

il f ....

Day 3

Listen again and write the words.

lo s

il s

la p

la b

l'u

Listen, repeat, and copy.

1. lo stadio
2. il supermercato
3. la palestra
4. la biblioteca
5. l'ufficio

Day 4

Listen again and write the words.

il c

la n

il t

la r

gli i

Listen, repeat, and copy.

1. il cielo
2. la nuvola
3. il terreno
4. la roccia
5. gli insetti

129

Day 5 What can you remember from this week?

1. Read the words and mark the correct pictures.

1 il computer

A ☐ B ☐

2 il sito web

A ☐ B ☐

3 le cuffie

A ☐ B ☐

4 il cellulare

A ☐ B ☐

5 il caricabatterie

A ☐ B ☐

2. Look at the pictures and write the correct words.

1 l'u _____

2 la b _____

3 lo s _____

4 la p _____

5 il s _____

3. Look at the pictures and circle the correct words.

① il fornello
la credenza

② il cestino
il fornello

③ il forno
il cestino

④ il frigorifero
la credenza

⑤ il forno
il frigorifero

4. Look at the pictures and fill in the missing letters.

① l _ r _ c _ i _

② i _ _ c _ e _ o

③ l _ _ n _ v _ l _

④ i _ _ t _ r _ a _ o

⑤ g _ i _ _ n _ e _ t _

Day 1

Listen, repeat, and copy.

① il fiocco di neve
....

② il pupazzo di neve
....

③ la palla di neve
....

④ la neve
....

⑤ il ghiaccio
....

Listen again and write the words.

il f ....

il p ....

la p ....

la n ....

il g ....

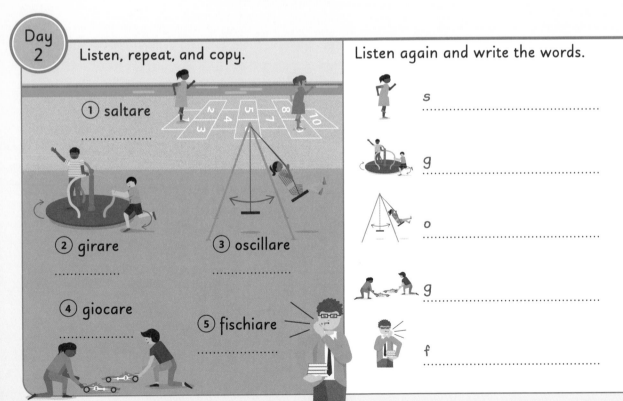

Day 2

Listen, repeat, and copy.

① saltare
....

② girare
....

③ oscillare
....

④ giocare
....

⑤ fischiare
....

Listen again and write the words.

s ....

g ....

o ....

g ....

f ....

Listen again and write the words.

la s ....

la f ....

il t ....

le s ....

il s ....

Listen, repeat, and copy.

① la strada
....

② la fermata dell'autobus
....

③ il traffico
....

④ le strisce pedonali
....

⑤ il semaforo
....

Listen again and write the words.

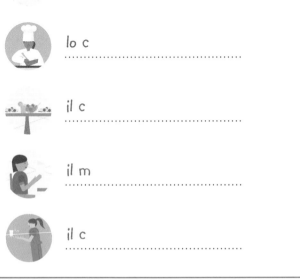

il r ....

lo c ....

il c ....

il m ....

il c ....

Listen, repeat, and copy.

① il ristorante
....

② lo chef
....

③ il cibo
....

④ il menù
....

⑤ il cameriere
....

133

Day 5

What can you remember from this week?

1. Read the words and mark the correct pictures.

1. il pupazzo di neve   A ☐   B ☐

2. la neve   A ☐   B ☐

3. il fioco di neve   A ☐   B ☐

4. la palla di neve   A ☐   B ☐

5. il ghiaccio   A ☐   B ☐

2. Look at the pictures and write the correct words.

1. il m ....

2. il r ....

3. lo c ....

4. il c ....

5. il c ....

Look at the pictures and write the letters in the correct order.

g r c a e i o

1 g _ _ _ _ _ _ _

s r e l t a a

2 s _ _ _ _ _ _ _

g r e r a i

3 g _ _ _ _ _ _

o l l s c r e i a

4 o _ _ _ _ _ _ _ _ _

f h a r i i s c e

5 f _ _ _ _ _ _ _ _ _

4. Match the pictures to the correct words.

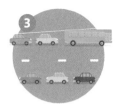

il traffico

le strisce
pedonali

la strada

il semaforo

la fermata
dell'autobus

Day 1

Listen, repeat, and copy.

1 la tazza

2 il piatto

3 la scodella

4 il bicchiere

5 la bottiglia

Listen again and write the words.

la t ....

il p ....

la s ....

il b ....

la b ....

Day 2

Listen, repeat, and copy.

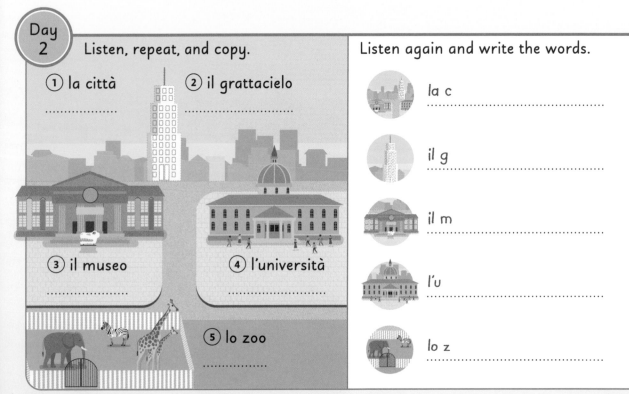

1 la città

2 il grattacielo

3 il museo

4 l'università

5 lo zoo

Listen again and write the words.

la c ....

il g ....

il m ....

l'u ....

lo z ....

Listen again and write the words.

i ....

g ....

g ....

f ....

f ....

Listen, repeat, and copy.

① iniziare
....

② guardare
....

③ gareggiare
....

④ finire
....

⑤ filmare
....

Listen again and write the words.

il p ....

il d ....

il c ....

il c ....

lo s ....

Listen, repeat, and copy.

① il portafogli
....

② il denaro
....

③ il carrello
....

④ il cesto
....

⑤ lo shopping
....

Week 33

Day 5

What can you remember from this week?

1. Look at the pictures and fill in the missing letters.

1) i _ p _ a _ t _

2) l _ b _ t _ i _ l _ a

3) i _ b _ c _ h _ e _ e

4) l _ s _ o _ e _ l _

5) l _ t _ z _ a

2. Read the words and mark the correct pictures.

1) guardare

A ☐   B ☐

2) finire

A ☐   B ☐

3) iniziare

A ☐   B ☐

4) gareggiare

A ☐   B ☐

5) filmare

A ☐   B ☐

138

3. Look at the pictures and circle the correct words.

il denaro

il portafogli

lo shopping

il cesto

il cesto

il carrello

lo shopping

il denaro

il portafogli

il carrello

4. Look at the pictures and write the correct words.

lo z ....

la c ....

il m ....

l'u ....

il g ....

Day 1

Listen, repeat, and copy.

① il picnic

....

② il sentiero

....

③ la coperta

....

④ il ponte

....

⑤ il ruscello

....

Listen again and write the words.

 il p ....

 il s ....

 la c ....

 il p ....

 il r ....

Day 2

Listen, repeat, and copy.

① il viaggio

....

② il panorama

....

③ la foto

....

④ la cartolina

....

⑤ la macchina fotografica

....

Listen again and write the words.

 il v ....

 il p ....

 la f ....

 la c ....

 la m ....

Listen again and write the words.

l ....

v ....

i ....

p ....

m ....

Listen, repeat, and copy.

① lavorare
....

② viaggiare
....

③ incontrare
....

④ parlare
....

⑤ mostrare
....

Listen again and write the words.

il s ....

la l ....

la t ....

il r ....

l'a ....

Listen, repeat, and copy.

① il sole
....

② la luna
....

③ la terra
....

④ il razzo
....

⑤ l'astronauta
....

Day 5 What can you remember from this week?

1. Look at the pictures and write the letters in the correct order.

1. v g r e g i a i a

   v _ _ _ _ _ _ _ _ _

2. l r a r e a v o

   l _ _ _ _ _ _ _

3. p r l r a e a

   p _ _ _ _ _ _

4. i t r a n r e c o n

   i _ _ _ _ _ _ _ _ _ _

5. m t r o s e a r

   m _ _ _ _ _ _ _

2. Look at the pictures and mark the correct words.

1. il sole ☐
   l'astronauta ☐
   la luna ☐

2. il razzo ☐
   la terra ☐
   l'astronauta ☐

3. il sole ☐
   la luna ☐
   la terra ☐

4. la luna ☐
   il razzo ☐
   l'astronauta ☐

5. il sole ☐
   la terra ☐
   il razzo ☐

3. Look at the pictures and write the correct words.

| il sentiero | il ponte | il picnic | il ruscello | la coperta |

1 il p ....

2 il r ....

3 il s ....

4 il p ....

5 la c ....

4. Look at the pictures and circle the correct words.

1 la foto
la macchina fotografica

2 la cartolina
il panorama

3 il viaggio
la macchina fotografica

4 il viaggio
il panorama

5 la foto
la cartolina

Day 1

Listen, repeat, and copy.

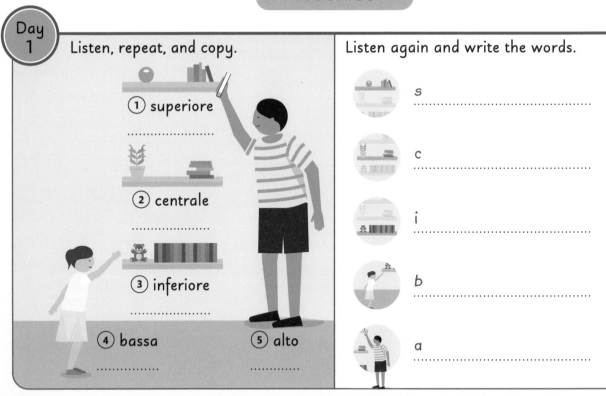

① superiore

② centrale

③ inferiore

④ bassa ⑤ alto

Listen again and write the words.

s ....

c ....

i ....

b ....

a ....

Day 2

Listen, repeat, and copy.

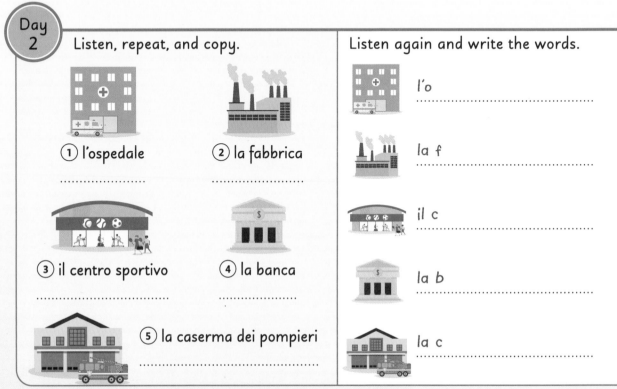

① l'ospedale ② la fabbrica

③ il centro sportivo ④ la banca

⑤ la caserma dei pompieri

Listen again and write the words.

l'o ....

la f ....

il c ....

la b ....

la c ....

Week 35

Listen again and write the words.

b ....

a ....

c ....

t ....

f ....

Listen, repeat, and copy.

① bagnata ....

② asciutto ....

③ caldo ....

④ torrido ....

⑤ freddo ....

Listen again and write the words.

p ....

s ....

r ....

s ....

l ....

Listen, repeat, and copy.

① prestare ....

② sussurrare ....

③ rovistare ....

④ studiare ....

⑤ leggere ....

Day 5

What can you remember from this week?

1. Read the words and mark the correct pictures.

1 la fabbrica

A ☐   B ☐

2 il centro sportivo

A ☐   B ☐

3 la banca

A ☐   B ☐

4 la caserma dei pompieri

A ☐   B ☐

5 l'ospedale

A ☐   B ☐

2. Look at the pictures and fill in the missing letters.

1

b _ s _ a

2

i _ f _ r _ o _ e

3

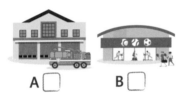

c _ n _ r _ l _

4

a _ t _

5

s _ p _ r _ o _ e

3. Look at the pictures and write the correct words.

1. c ....

2. a ....

3. b ....

4. f ....

5. t ....

4. Match the pictures to the correct words.

1. sussurrare

2. studiare

3. prestare

4. rovistare

5. leggere

Week 36

Day 1

Listen, repeat, and copy.

① il tè
....

② il latte
....

③ lo zucchero
....

④ il caffè
....

⑤ il biscotto
....

Listen again and write the words.

il t
....

il l
....

lo z
....

il c
....

il b
....

Day 2

Listen, repeat, and copy.

① decollare
....

② atterrare
....

③ scendere
....

④ salire
....

⑤ sbrigarsi
....

Listen again and write the words.

d
....

a
....

s
....

s
....

s
....

Listen again and write the words.

i p

la s

la m

gli s

lo s

Listen, repeat, and copy.

① i pattini da ghiaccio

② la slitta

③ la mazza da hockey

④ gli sci

⑤ lo snowboard

Listen again and write the words.

l'o

l'a

il b

la g

il v

Listen, repeat, and copy.

① l'oro

② l'argento

③ il bronzo

④ la gara

⑤ il vincitore

Week 36

Day 5 What can you remember from this week?

---

1. Look at the pictures and write the correct words.

> il latte   il tè   il caffè
> lo zucchero   il biscotto

 **1** il t ....

 **2** il b ....

 **3** il c ....

 4 il l ....

5 lo z ....

---

2. Look at the pictures and circle the correct words.

 **1**   la gara / l'oro

 **2**   il vincitore / l'argento

 **3**   l'argento / l'oro

 **4**   il vincitore / il bronzo

 **5**   il bronzo / la gara

3. Look at the pictures and fill in the missing letters.

1 d c _ l _ a _ e

2 _ t _ e _ r _ r _

3 s _ r _ g _ r _ i

4 s _ e _ d _ r _

5 _ a _ i _ e

4. Read the words and mark the correct pictures.

1 gli sci

A ☐   B ☐

2 i pattini da ghiaccio

A ☐   B ☐

3 la slitta

A ☐   B ☐

4 la mazza da hockey

A ☐   B ☐

5 lo snowboard

A ☐   B ☐

Day 1

Listen, repeat, and copy.

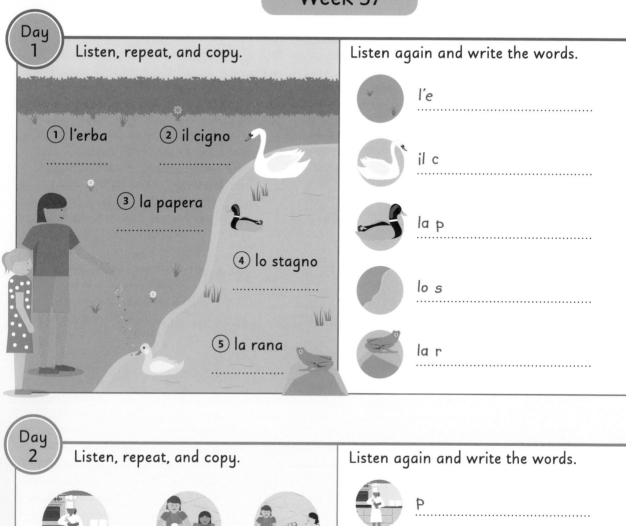

① l'erba ....

② il cigno ....

③ la papera ....

④ lo stagno ....

⑤ la rana ....

Listen again and write the words.

l'e ....

il c ....

la p ....

lo s ....

la r ....

Day 2

Listen, repeat, and copy.

① preparare ....

② ordinare ....

③ pagare ....

④ piacere ....

⑤ non piacere ....

Listen again and write the words.

 p ....

 o ....

 p ....

 p ....

 n ....

Listen again and write the words.

l'o ....

il t ....

la f ....

il p ....

la r ....

Listen, repeat, and copy.

① l'orso polare ....

② il tricheco ....

③ la foca ....

④ il pinguino ....

⑤ la renna ....

Listen again and write the words.

il p ....

i g ....

gli o ....

il p ....

la s ....

Listen, repeat, and copy.

① il profumo ....

② i gioielli ....

③ gli occhiali ....

④ il pettine ....

⑤ la spazzola ....

Week 37

Day 5

What can you remember from this week?

1. Look at the pictures and write the correct words.

| pagare | non piacere | piacere | ordinare | preparare |

1 p ....

2 n ....

3 p ....

4 o ....

5 p ....

2. Match the pictures to the correct words.

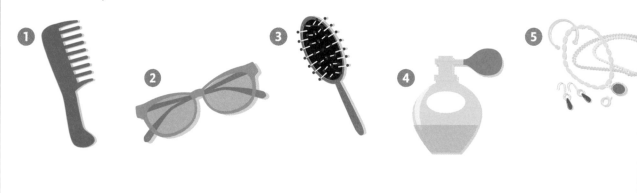

la spazzola   il pettine   i gioielli   gli occhiali   il profumo

. Look at the pictures and mark
the correct words.

1
il pinguino ☐
il tricheco ☐

2
l'orso polare ☐
il pinguino ☐

3
la renna ☐
la foca ☐

4
la renna ☐
l'orso polare ☐

5
la foca ☐
il tricheco ☐

4. Look at the pictures and write
the correct words.

1
l'e ....

2
la r ....

3
lo s ....

4
il c ....

5
la p ....

Day 1

Listen, repeat, and copy.

① l'insalata

....

② il pomodoro ③ il formaggio

....

④ le olive ⑤ la lattuga

....

Listen again and write the words.

l'i

....

il p

....

il f

....

le o

....

la l

....

Day 2

Listen, repeat, and copy.

① castani

....

③ neri

....

④ grigi

....

② biondi

....

⑤ rossi

....

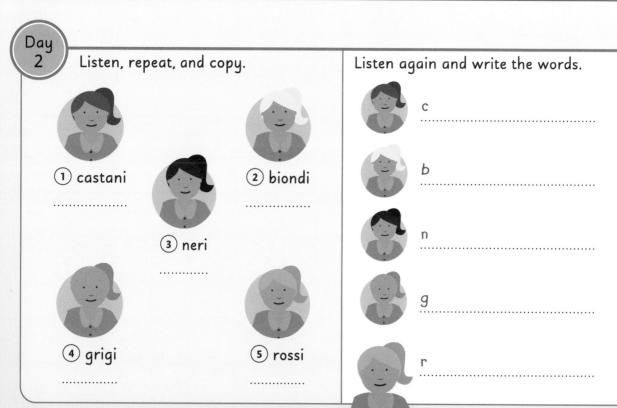

Listen again and write the words.

c

....

b

....

n

....

g

....

r

....

Listen again and write the words.

a ....

a ....

p ....

v ....

d ....

Listen, repeat, and copy.

1 arrivare ....

2 accogliere ....

3 portare ....

4 visitare ....

5 dare ....

Listen again and write the words.

l'a ....

l'a ....

il p ....

la v ....

la v ....

Listen, repeat, and copy.

1 l'aeroporto ....

2 l'aeroplano ....

3 il pilota ....

4 la vacanza ....

5 la valigia ....

Day 5

What can you remember from this week?

1. Look at the pictures and mark the correct words.

① l'aeroplano ☐
il pilota ☐
la vacanza ☐

② la valigia ☐
l'aeroplano ☐
l'aeroporto ☐

③ la vacanza ☐
la valigia ☐
il pilota ☐

④ la vacanza ☐
la valigia ☐
l'aeroporto ☐

⑤ il pilota ☐
l'aeroporto ☐
l'aeroplano ☐

2. Look at the pictures and write the letters in the correct order.

① p r t o e a r

p _ _ _ _ _ _ _

② a v a r r e r i

a _ _ _ _ _ _ _ _

③ v t a i r e s i

v _ _ _ _ _ _ _ _

④ d r e a

d _ _ _ _

⑤ a g c c o r l e i e

a _ _ _ _ _ _ _ _ _ _

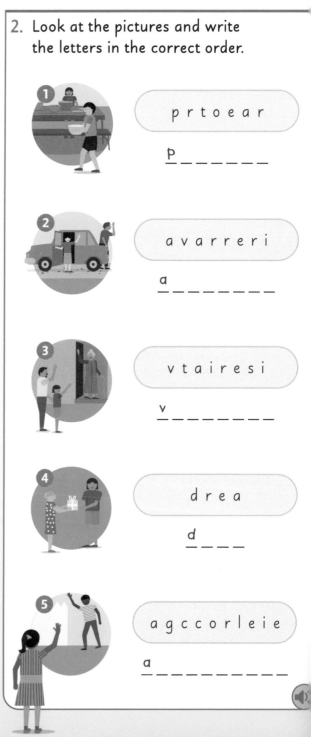

. Look at the pictures and write the correct words.

| grigi | biondi | neri | rossi | castani |

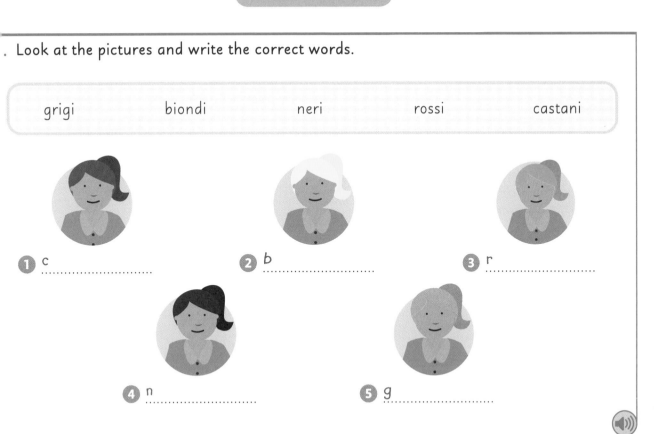

1 c ....

2 b ....

3 r ....

4 n ....

5 g ....

. Look at the picture and write the correct words.

le olive

il formaggio

l'insalata

il pomodoro

la lattuga

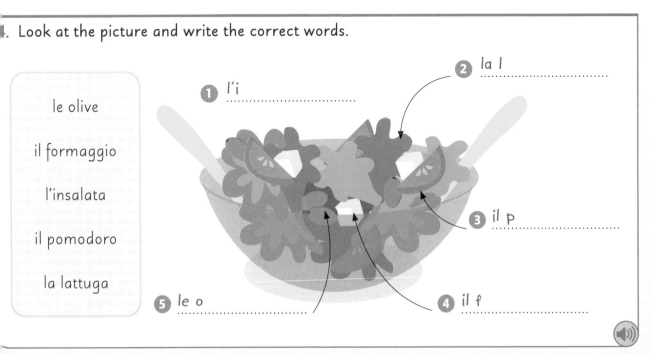

1 l'i ....

2 la l ....

3 il p ....

4 il f ....

5 le o ....

Week 39

Day 1

Listen, repeat, and copy.

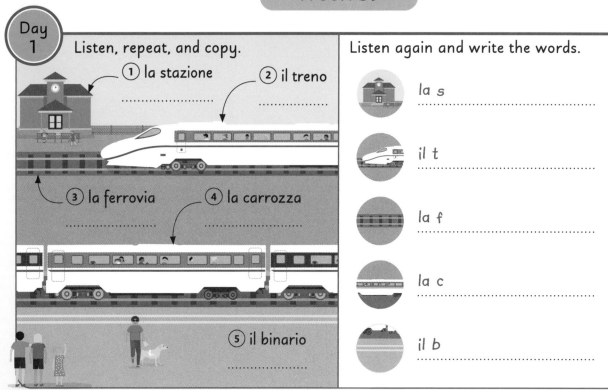

1. la stazione
....

2. il treno
....

3. la ferrovia
....

4. la carrozza
....

5. il binario
....

Listen again and write the words.

la s ....

il t ....

la f ....

la c ....

il b ....

Day 2

Listen, repeat, and copy.

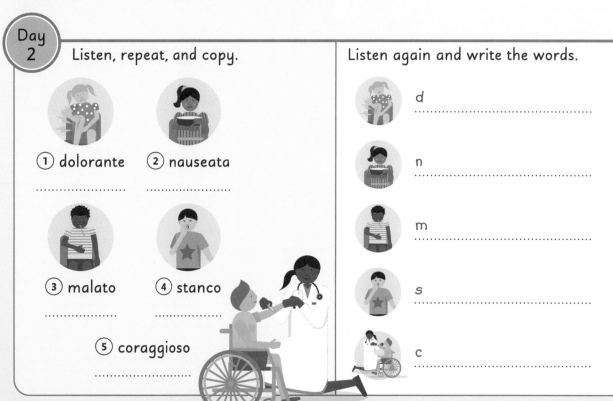

1. dolorante
....

2. nauseata
....

3. malato
....

4. stanco
....

5. coraggioso
....

Listen again and write the words.

d ....

n ....

m ....

s ....

c ....

Listen again and write the words.

la p ....

il p ....

il c ....

il g ....

la s ....

Listen, repeat, and copy.

① la partita ....

② il punteggio ....

③ il calcio ....

④ il giocatore ....

⑤ la squadra ....

Listen again and write the words.

la f ....

la m ....

il r ....

lo s ....

la c ....

Listen, repeat, and copy.

① la farfalla ....

② la mosca ....

③ il ragno ....

④ lo scarabeo ....

⑤ la chiocciola

Day 5

What can you remember from this week?

1. Look at the pictures and circle the correct words.

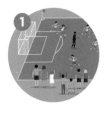

la partita
la squadra

il calcio
il punteggio

il calcio
la squadra

il giocatore
il punteggio

il giocatore
la partita

2. Look at the pictures and fill in the missing letters.

① l _ s _ a _ a _ e _

② _ a _ o _ c _

③ l _ f _ r _ a _ l _

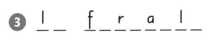

④ l _ c _ i _ c _ i _ l _

⑤ i _ _ r _ g _ o _

3. Look at the pictures and write the letters in the correct order.

1. c g o r i o a o g s

c _ _ _ _ _ _ _ _ _

2. n t a e a a u s

n _ _ _ _ _ _ _

3. d r o l n t o a e

d _ _ _ _ _ _ _ _

4. s n c o t a

s _ _ _ _ _

5. m t a o l a

m _ _ _ _ _

4. Read the words and mark the correct pictures.

1. il treno   A ☐   B ☐

2. la stazione   A ☐   B ☐

3. il binario   A ☐   B ☐

4. la ferrovia   A ☐   B ☐

5. la carrozza   A ☐   B ☐

Week 40

Day 1

Listen, repeat, and copy.

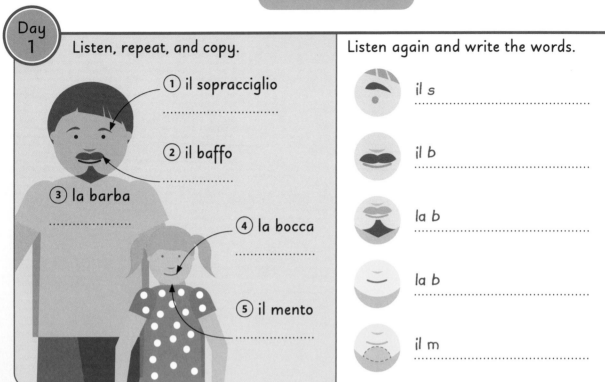

① il sopracciglio

....

② il baffo

....

③ la barba

....

④ la bocca

....

⑤ il mento

....

Listen again and write the words.

il s ....

il b ....

la b ....

la b ....

il m ....

Day 2

Listen, repeat, and copy.

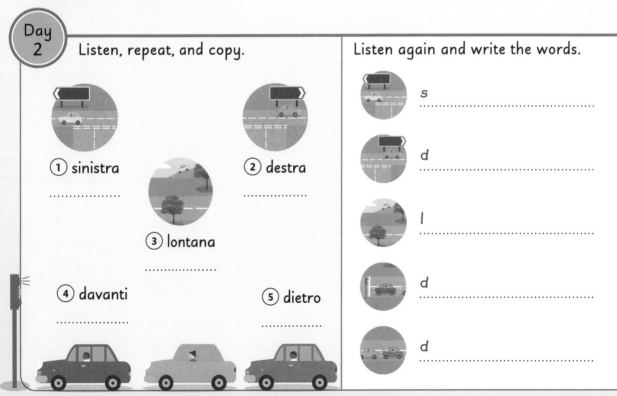

① sinistra

....

② destra

....

③ lontana

....

④ davanti

....

⑤ dietro

....

Listen again and write the words.

s ....

d ....

l ....

d ....

d ....

Listen again and write the words.

r ....

r ....

n ....

d ....

þ ....

Listen, repeat, and copy.

① rompere
....

② riportare
....

③ nascondersi
....

④ dare da mangiare
....

⑤ prendersi cura
....

Listen again and write the words.

c ....

s ....

s ....

a ....

r ....

Listen, repeat, and copy.

① chiaro
....

② scuro
....

③ sveglio
....

④ addormentato
....

⑤ rumoroso
....

Day 5

What can you remember from this week?

1. Look at the pictures and write the letters in the correct order.

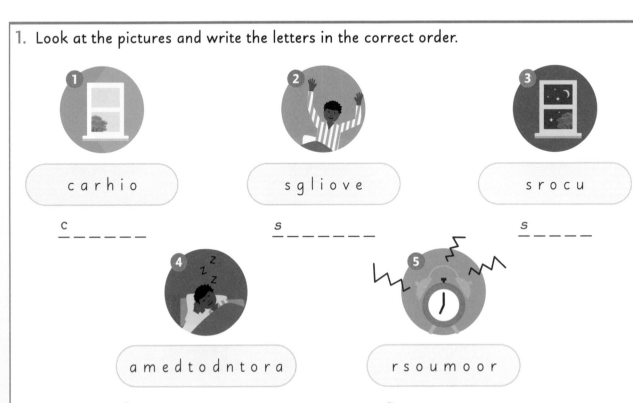

1. carhio

c _ _ _ _ _ _

2. sgliove

s _ _ _ _ _ _ _

3. srocu

s _ _ _ _ _

4. amedtodntora

a _ _ _ _ _ _ _ _ _ _ _ _

5. rsoumoor

r _ _ _ _ _ _ _

2. Match the pictures to the correct words.

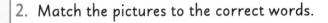

riportare   nascondersi   prendersi cura   dare da mangiare   rompere

3. Look at the pictures and mark the correct words.

1. lontana ☐
   destra ☐

2. dietro ☐
   sinistra ☐

3. lontana ☐
   dietro ☐

4. davanti ☐
   destra ☐

5. davanti ☐
   sinistra ☐

4. Look at the pictures and write the correct words.

il sopracciglio   la bocca   il mento
il baffo   la barba

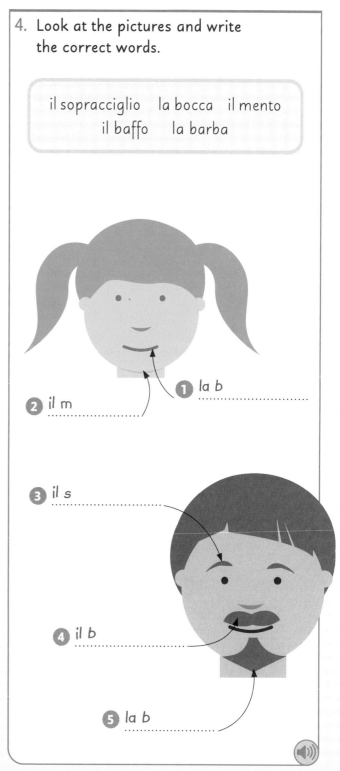

1 la b ....

2 il m ....

3 il s ....

4 il b ....

5 la b ....

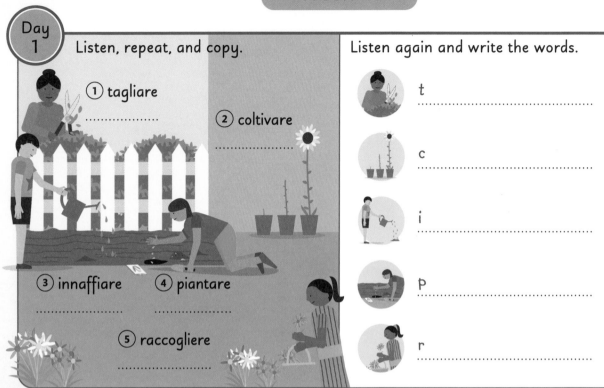

Day 1

Listen, repeat, and copy.

① tagliare

② coltivare

③ innaffiare ④ piantare

⑤ raccogliere

Listen again and write the words.

t ....

c ....

i ....

p ....

r ....

Day 2

Listen, repeat, and copy.

① la musica ② il gruppo musicale

③ il musicista ④ la pop star

⑤ il festival

Listen again and write the words.

la m ....

il g ....

il m ....

la p ....

il f ....

Listen again and write the words.

la m
....

il q
....

l'i
....

l'a
....

il c
....

Listen, repeat, and copy.

① la metà
....

② il quarto
....

③ l'intero
....

④ l'angolo
....

⑤ il centro
....

Listen again and write the words.

l'a
....

il l
....

gli o
....

la p
....

il c
....

Listen, repeat, and copy.

① l'albergo
....

② il lettino
....

③ gli occhiali
da sole
....

④ la piscina
....

⑤ il cappello
....

Day 5 What can you remember from this week?

1. Look at the pictures and write the correct words.

> il centro   l'intero   la metà
> l'angolo   il quarto

1 l'i ....

2 l'a ....

3 la m ....

4 il c ....

5 il q ....

2. Look at the pictures and circle the correct words.

1 gli occhiali da sole
la piscina

2 il cappello
il lettino

3 l'albergo
la piscina

4 il lettino
l'albergo

5 il cappello
gli occhiali da sole

3. Read the words and mark the correct pictures.

1 il festival

A ☐   B ☐

2 il musicista

A ☐   B ☐

3 la musica

A ☐   B ☐

4 la pop star

A ☐   B ☐

5 il gruppo musicale

A ☐   B ☐

4. Look at the pictures and write the correct words.

1 r ....

2 p ....

3 i ....

4 c ....

5 t ....

Day 1

Listen, repeat, and copy.

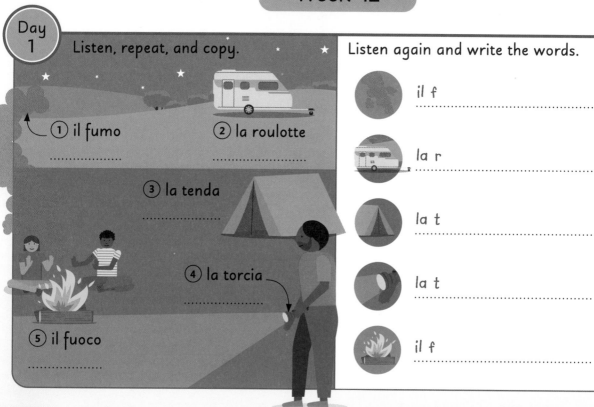

① il fumo

② la roulotte

③ la tenda

④ la torcia

⑤ il fuoco

Listen again and write the words.

il f

la r

la t

la t

il f

Day 2

Listen, repeat, and copy.

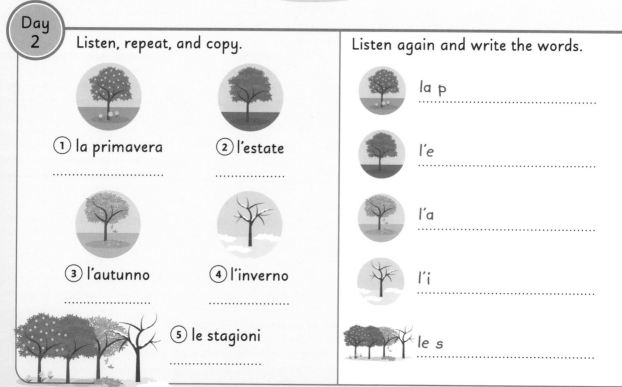

① la primavera

② l'estate

③ l'autunno

④ l'inverno

⑤ le stagioni

Listen again and write the words.

la p

l'e

l'a

l'i

le s

Week 42

Listen again and write the words.

`12:01` l'o ....

`12:00` l'o ....

`12:01` il m ....

il m ....

la m ....

Listen, repeat, and copy.

① l'orologio
....

`12:01`

② l'ora ....   ③ il minuto ....

④ il mezzogiorno ....   ⑤ la mezzanotte ....

Listen again and write the words.

il t ....

la m ....

la c ....

la c ....

gli a ....

Listen, repeat, and copy.

① il tecnico ....

② la macchina ....

③ la cassetta degli attrezzi ....   ④ la colla ....

⑤ gli attrezzi ....

Day 5

What can you remember from this week?

1. Look at the pictures and fill in the missing letters.

1 l'_ _ r _ l _ g _ o

2 _ _l _ _ _ e _ z _ g _ o _ n _

3 i _ _ m _ n _ t _

4 _ l _ _ m _ z _ a _ o _ t _

5 l'_ r _ _ _ _

2. Look at the pictures and circle the correct words.

1
il fuoco
la tenda

2
il fumo
la roulotte

3
la tenda
la torcia

4
la roulotte
la torcia

5
il fumo
il fuoco

3. Look at the pictures and write the correct words.

1. l'e ....

2. l'i ....

3. l'a ....

4. la p ....

5. le s ....

4. Match the pictures to the correct words.

1. la cassetta degli attrezzi

2. la macchina

3. la colla

4. il tecnico

5. gli attrezzi

175

Day 1

Listen, repeat, and copy.

① portare ....

② pesare ....

③ vendere ....

④ comprare ....

⑤ dare ....

Listen again and write the words.

p ....

p ....

v ....

c ....

d ....

Day 2

Listen, repeat, and copy.

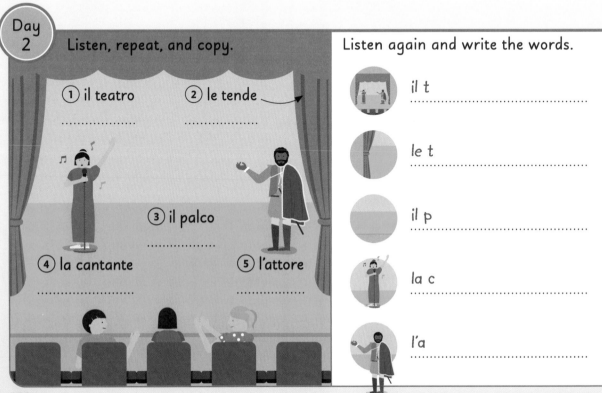

① il teatro ....

② le tende ....

③ il palco ....

④ la cantante ....

⑤ l'attore ....

Listen again and write the words.

il t ....

le t ....

il p ....

la c ....

l'a ....

Day 3

Listen again and write the words.

la b ....

il p ....

la p ....

il c ....

il s ....

Listen, repeat, and copy.

① la bandiera
....

② il pallone da spiaggia
....

③ la paletta
....

④ il castello di sabbia
....

⑤ il secchiello
....

Day 4

Listen again and write the words.

la s ....

il f ....

il m ....

l'a ....

l'a ....

Listen, repeat, and copy.

① la settimana
....

② il fine settimana
....

③ il mese
....

④ l'anno
....

⑤ l'agenda
....

Day 5 What can you remember from this week?

1. Look at the pictures and write the letters in the correct order.

p r a e e s

p _ _ _ _ _ _

c p r a r e o m

c _ _ _ _ _ _ _ _

d r e a

d _ _ _

v d e e r e n

v _ _ _ _ _ _ _

p t a r e o r

p _ _ _ _ _ _ _

2. Look at the pictures and circle the correct words.

il teatro

l'attore

le tende

la cantante

l'attore

il palco

la cantante

il palco

le tende

il teatro

3. Match the pictures to the correct words.

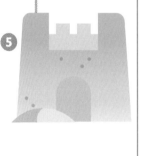

il secchiello   la bandiera   il castello
di sabbia   il pallone
da spiaggia   la paletta

4. Look at the pictures and write the correct words.

la settimana   il mese   il fine settimana   l'anno   l'agenda

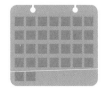

① il m ....

② la s ....

③ l'a ....

④ l'a ....

⑤ il f ....

Day 1

Listen, repeat, and copy.

Listen again and write the words.

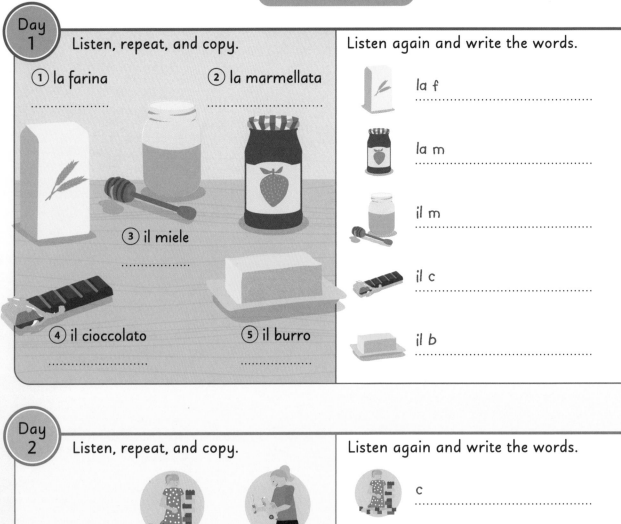

① la farina

② la marmellata

③ il miele

④ il cioccolato

⑤ il burro

la f ....

la m ....

il m ....

il c ....

il b ....

Day 2

Listen, repeat, and copy.

Listen again and write the words.

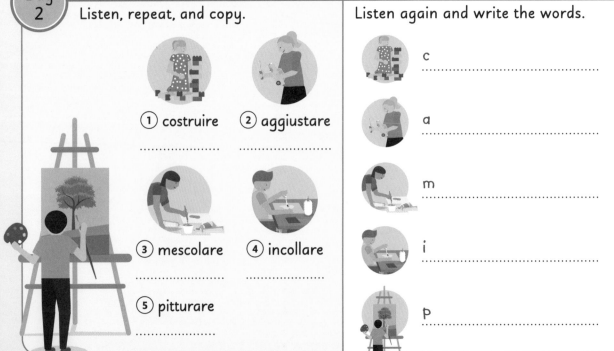

① costruire

② aggiustare

③ mescolare

④ incollare

⑤ pitturare

c ....

a ....

m ....

i ....

p ....

Listen again and write the words.

l'o ....

i ....

m ....

a ....

s ....

Listen, repeat, and copy.

① l'orario
....

② inglese
....

③ matematica
....

④ arte e immagine
....

⑤ scienze
....

Listen again and write the words.

l ....

v ....

m ....

g ....

p ....

Listen, repeat, and copy.

① lento
....

② veloce
....

③ magro
....

④ grasso
....

⑤ peloso
....

Week 44

Day 5

What can you remember from this week?

---

1. Look at the pictures and circle the correct words.

 **1**
inglese
arte e immagine

 **2**
matematica
scienze

  3
l'orario
scienze

4
inglese
matematica

5
arte e immagine
l'orario

---

2. Look at the pictures and fill in the missing letters.

 **1**
c s r i e
_ _ _ r _ i e

 **2**
p t u a e
p _ t _ u _ a _ e

 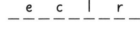 **3**
e c l r
_ e _ c _ l _ r _

 **4**
a g u t r
a _ g _ u _ t _ r _

 **5**
n o l r
_ n _ o _ l _ r _

3. Look at the pictures and mark the correct words.

1. la marmellata ☐
   il burro ☐
   il cioccolato ☐

2. la farina ☐
   il miele ☐
   la marmellata ☐

3. il burro ☐
   il cioccolato ☐
   il miele ☐

4. la farina ☐
   il burro ☐
   la marmellata ☐

5. il miele ☐
   il cioccolato ☐
   la farina ☐

4. Look at the pictures and write the correct words.

lento   peloso   veloce
grasso   magro

1. p.............................

2. l.............................

3. g.............................

4. v.............................

5. m.............................

183

Day 1

Listen, repeat, and copy.

① la mappa
....

② il quaderno
....

③ il dizionario
....

④ gli scacchi
....

⑤ lo studente
....

Listen again and write the words.

la m
....

il q
....

il d
....

gli s
....

lo s
....

Day 2

Listen, repeat, and copy.

① l'entrata
....

② l'uscita
....

③ il parcheggio
....

④ i negozi
....

⑤ il centro commerciale
....

Listen again and write the words.

l'e
....

l'u
....

il p
....

i n
....

il c
....

Day 3

Listen again and write the words.

la m
....

la f
....

la r
....

il c
....

la m
....

Listen, repeat, and copy.

① la mascherina
....

② la fasciatura
....

③ la radiografia
....

④ il cerotto
....

⑤ la medicina
....

Day 4

Listen again and write the words.

a
....

r
....

c
....

b
....

d
....

Listen, repeat, and copy.

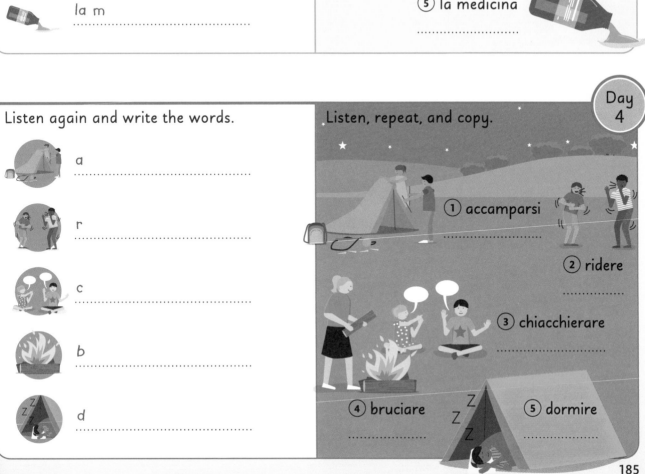

① accamparsi
....

② ridere
....

③ chiacchierare
....

④ bruciare
....

⑤ dormire
....

Day 5

What can you remember from this week?

1. Look at the pictures and circle the correct words.

l'entrata
l'uscita

il parcheggio
il centro commerciale

i negozi
il parcheggio

l'entrata
i negozi

l'uscita
il centro commerciale

2. Look at the pictures and write the correct words.

lo s ....

la m ....

gli s ....

il d ....

il q ....

Week 45

3. Look at the pictures and mark the correct words.

1. la medicina ☐
   la mascherina ☐

2. il cerotto ☐
   la radiografia ☐

3. la radiografia ☐
   la fasciatura ☐

4. la medicina ☐
   il cerotto ☐

5. la mascherina ☐
   la fasciatura ☐

4. Look at the pictures and fill in the missing letters.

1. b _ u _ i _ r _

2. r _ d _ r _

3. c _ i _ c _ h _ e _ a _ e

4. a _ c _ m _ a _ s _

5. d _ r _ i _ e

Week 46

Day 1

Listen, repeat, and copy.

① il gufo

② lo scoiattolo

③ il cervo

④ il lupo

⑤ la volpe

Listen again and write the words.

il g ....

lo s ....

il c ....

il l ....

la v ....

Day 2

Listen, repeat, and copy.

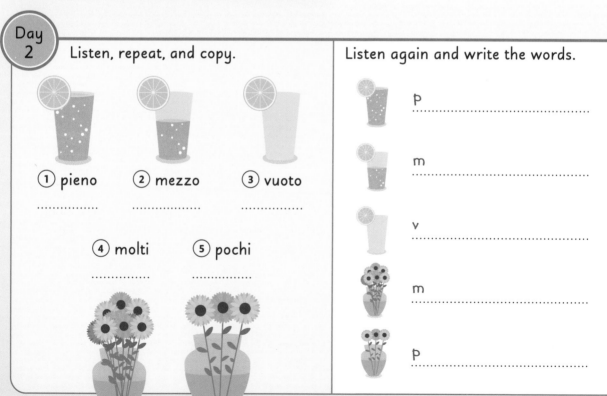

① pieno

② mezzo

③ vuoto

④ molti

⑤ pochi

Listen again and write the words.

p ....

m ....

v ....

m ....

p ....

Listen again and write the words.

il g
....

le a
....

la s
....

le r
....

la c
....

Listen, repeat, and copy.

① il granchio
....

② le alghe
....

③ la stella marina
....

④ le rocce
....

⑤ la conchiglia
....

Listen again and write the words.

il q
....

la r
....

il f
....

la r
....

la v
....

Listen, repeat, and copy.

① il quotidiano
....

② la rivista
....

③ il fumetto
....

④ la rivista
di enigmistica
....

⑤ la vignetta
....

Day 5

What can you remember from this week?

1. Look at the pictures and write the correct words.

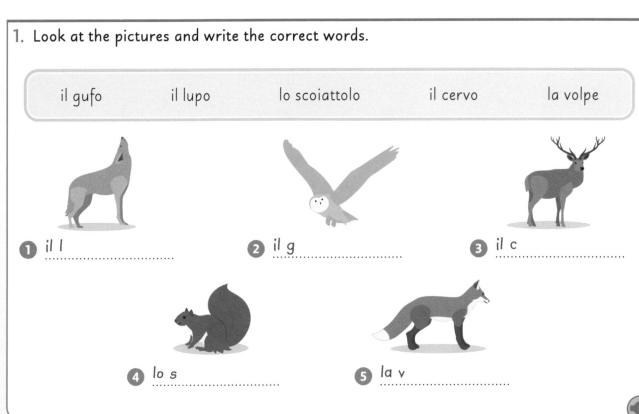

| il gufo | il lupo | lo scoiattolo | il cervo | la volpe |

1 il l ....

2 il g ....

3 il c ....

4 lo s ....

5 la v ....

2. Match the pictures to the correct words.

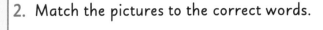

1   2   3   4   5

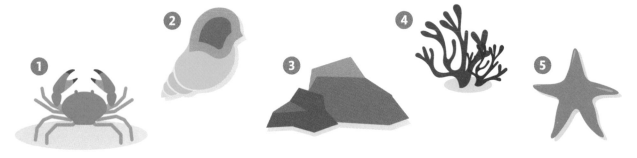

la conchiglia   il granchio   la stella marina   le rocce   le alghe

3. Look at the pictures and write
the correct words.

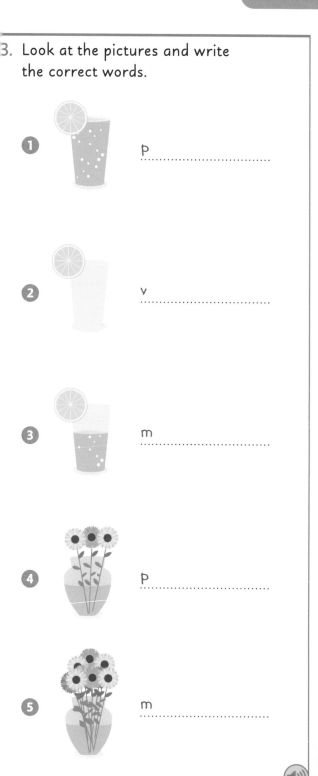

1 p ....

2 v ....

3 m ....

4 p ....

5 m ....

4. Read the words and mark
the correct pictures.

1 la rivista   A ☐   B ☐

2 la rivista di
  enigmistica   A ☐   B ☐

3 il quotidiano   A ☐   B ☐

4 il fumetto   A ☐   B ☐

5 la vignetta   A ☐   B ☐

Day 1

Listen, repeat, and copy.

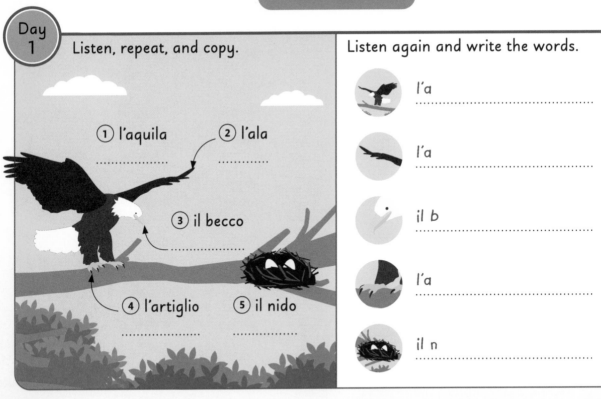

① l'aquila   ② l'ala

③ il becco

④ l'artiglio   ⑤ il nido

Listen again and write the words.

l'a ....

l'a ....

il b ....

l'a ....

il n ....

Day 2

Listen, repeat, and copy.

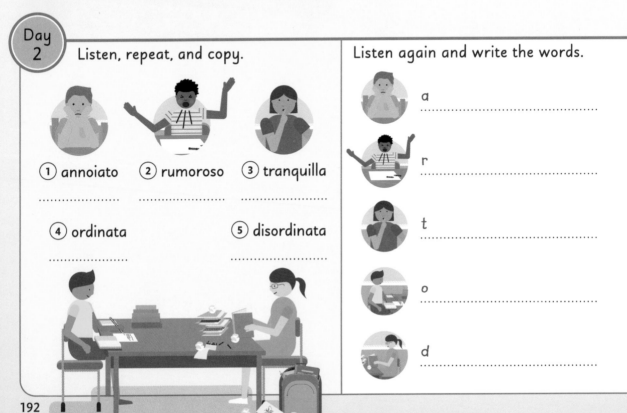

① annoiato   ② rumoroso   ③ tranquilla

④ ordinata   ⑤ disordinata

Listen again and write the words.

a ....

r ....

t ....

o ....

d ....

Listen again and write the words.

lo s ....

lo s ....

l'h ....

il p ....

lo s ....

Listen, repeat, and copy.

① lo sci
....

② lo slittino
....

③ l'hockey sul ghiaccio
....

④ il pattinaggio sul ghiaccio
....

⑤ lo snowboard
....

Listen again and write the words.

s ....

g ....

t ....

l ....

le m ....

Listen, repeat, and copy.

① storia
....

② geografia
....

③ tecnologia
....

④ lingue straniere
....

⑤ le materie
....

Day 5

What can you remember from this week?

1. Look at the pictures and mark the correct words.

① geografia ☐
le materie ☐

② lingue straniere ☐
tecnologia ☐

③ storia ☐
geografia ☐

④ lingue straniere ☐
storia ☐

⑤ tecnologia ☐
le materie ☐

2. Look at the pictures and fill in the missing letters.

① i _ n _ d _

② _ l _ e _ c

③ l' _ l _

④ _ a _ t _ g _ i _ _

⑤ l' _ q _ i _ a

3. Look at the pictures and write the correct words.

1 r

2 t ....

3 d ....

4 o ....

5 a ....

4. Read the words and mark the correct pictures.

1 lo slittino

A ☐   B ☐

2 lo snowboard

A ☐   B ☐

3 lo sci

A ☐   B ☐

4 il pattinaggio sul ghiaccio

A ☐   B ☐

5 l'hockey sul ghiaccio

A ☐   B ☐

Week 48

Day 1

Listen, repeat, and copy.

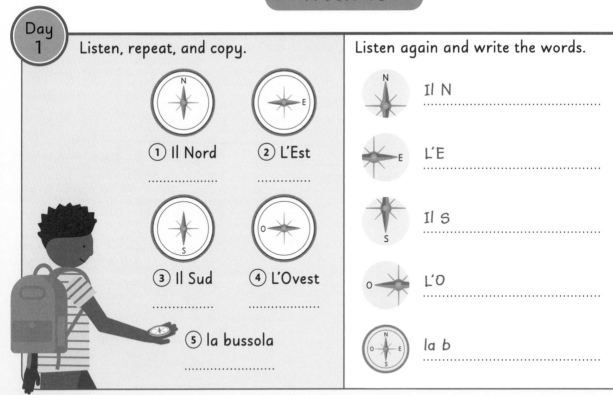

1. Il Nord
2. L'Est
3. Il Sud
4. L'Ovest
5. la bussola

Listen again and write the words.

Il N ....

L'E ....

Il S ....

L'O ....

la b ....

Day 2

Listen, repeat, and copy.

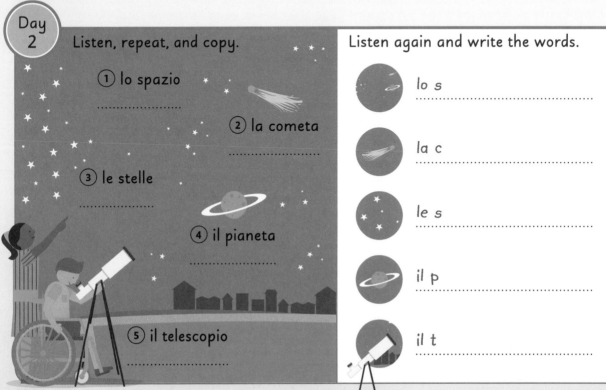

1. lo spazio
2. la cometa
3. le stelle
4. il pianeta
5. il telescopio

Listen again and write the words.

lo s ....

la c ....

le s ....

il p ....

il t ....

Listen again and write the words.

la c ....

la b ....

l'a ....

il b ....

l'o ....

Listen, repeat, and copy.

① la collana ....

② la borsa ....

③ l'anello ....

④ il braccialetto ....

⑤ l'orologio ....

Listen again and write the words.

il g ....

la s ....

l'a ....

la f ....

le p ....

Listen, repeat, and copy.

① il giornalista ....

② la stilista ....

③ l'artista ....

④ la fotografa ....

⑤ le professioni ....

Day 5

What can you remember from this week?

1. **Look at the picture and write the correct words.**

L'Ovest
Il Nord
la bussola
Il Sud
L'Est

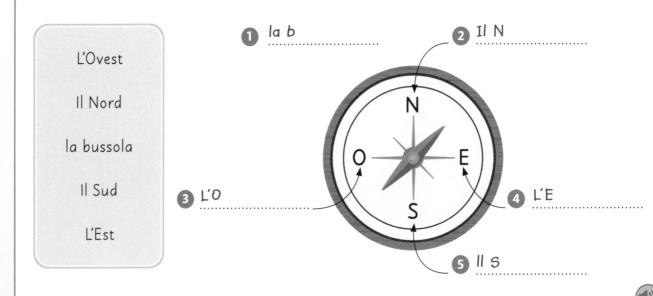

1 la b ....

2 Il N ....

3 L'O ....

4 L'E ....

5 Il S ....

2. **Look at the pictures and circle the correct words.**

1 le professioni
l'artista

2 la fotografa
la stilista

3 il giornalista
la stilista

4 l'artista
il giornalista

5 le professioni
la fotografa

3. Match the pictures to the correct words.

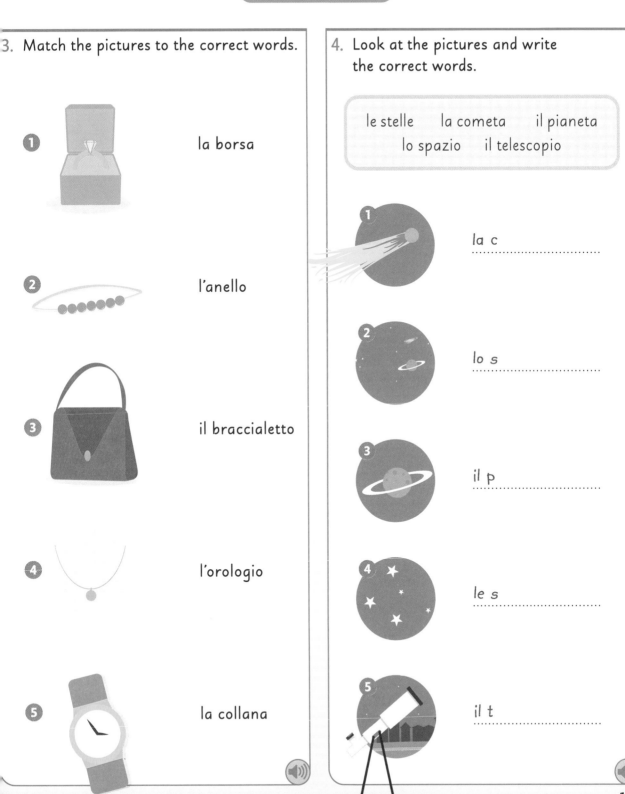

1 la borsa

2 l'anello

3 il braccialetto

4 l'orologio

5 la collana

4. Look at the pictures and write the correct words.

le stelle   la cometa   il pianeta
lo spazio   il telescopio

1 la c ....

2 lo s ....

3 il p ....

4 le s ....

5 il t ....

199

Day 1

Listen, repeat, and copy.

① i baffi
....

② il collare
....

③ la pelliccia
....

④ la zampa
....

⑤ la coda
....

Listen again and write the words.

 i b ....

 il c ....

 la p ....

 la z ....

 la c ....

Day 2

Listen, repeat, and copy.

① inventare
....

② progettare
....

③ pensare
....

④ recitare
....

⑤ esplorare
....

Listen again and write the words.

 i ....

 p ....

 p ....

 r ....

 e ....

Day 3

Listen again and write the words.

la p ....

il m ....

la l ....

il l ....

la p ....

Listen, repeat, and copy.

① la plastica
....

② il metallo
....

③ la lana
....

④ il legno
....

⑤ la pietra
....

Day 4

Listen again and write the words.

le b ....

il p ....

il c ....

la f ....

il c ....

Listen, repeat, and copy.

① le bacchette
....

② il pasto
....

③ il coltello
....

④ la forchetta ⑤ il cucchiaio
....

Week 49

Day 5

What can you remember from this week?

1. Read the words and mark the correct pictures.

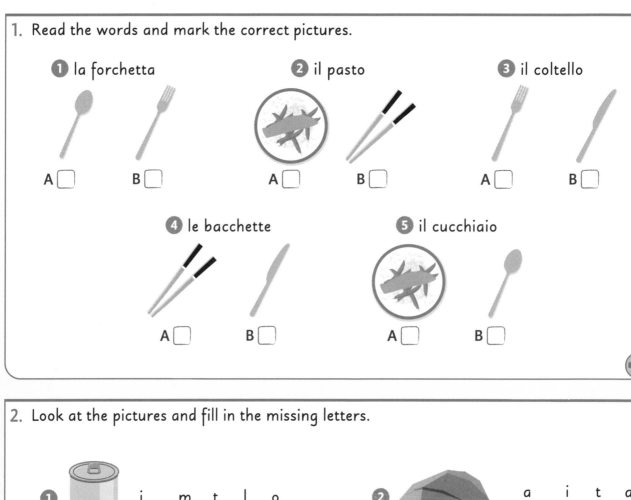

1 la forchetta   **2** il pasto   **3** il coltello

A ☐   B ☐   A ☐   B ☐   A ☐   B ☐

4 le bacchette   **5** il cucchiaio

A ☐   B ☐   A ☐   B ☐

2. Look at the pictures and fill in the missing letters.

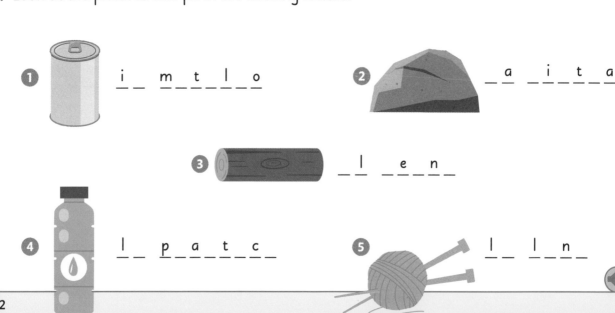

1 i _ m _ t _ l _ o

2 _ a _ i _ t _ a

3 _ _ l _ _ e _ n _

4 l _ p _ a _ t _ c _

5 l _ _ l _ n _

3. Look at the pictures and mark the correct words.

1. il collare ☐
   i baffi ☐
   la pelliccia ☐

2. il collare ☐
   la coda ☐
   la zampa ☐

3. la coda ☐
   la pelliccia ☐
   i baffi ☐

4. i baffi ☐
   il collare ☐
   la zampa ☐

5. la pelliccia ☐
   la zampa ☐
   la coda ☐

4. Look at the pictures and write the letters in the correct order.

1. i t a n r e v e n
   i _ _ _ _ _ _ _ _

2. p s a r e e n
   p _ _ _ _ _ _

3. e s p r e a l o r
   e _ _ _ _ _ _ _ _

4. r e a e r c i t
   r _ _ _ _ _ _ _

5. p g e t a r t r o e
   p _ _ _ _ _ _ _ _ _

Day 1

Listen, repeat, and copy.

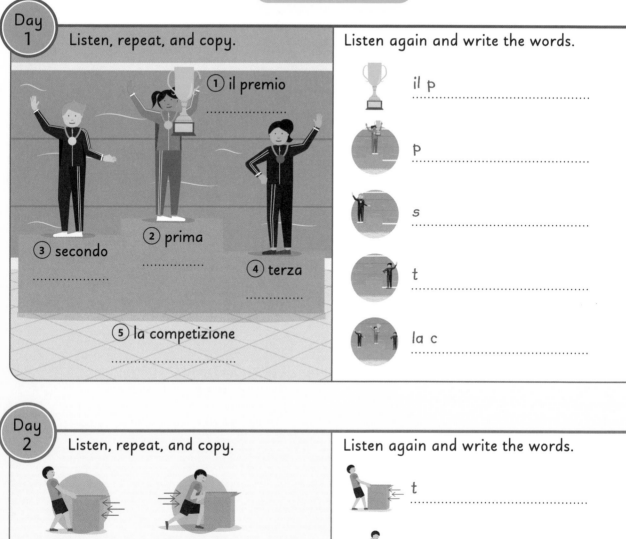

1. il premio
2. prima
3. secondo
4. terza
5. la competizione

Listen again and write the words.

il p ....

p ....

s ....

t ....

la c ....

Day 2

Listen, repeat, and copy.

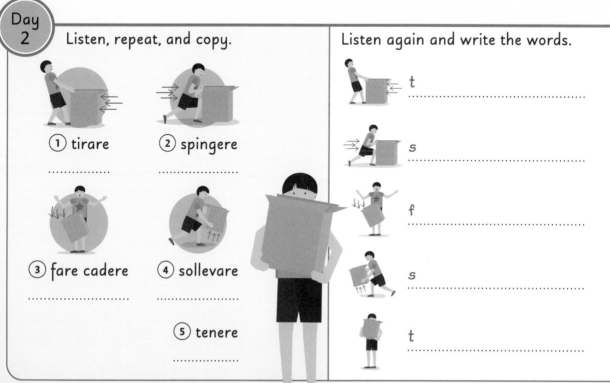

1. tirare
2. spingere
3. fare cadere
4. sollevare
5. tenere

Listen again and write the words.

t ....

s ....

f ....

s ....

t ....

Listen again and write the words.

l'i
....

il p
....

la r
....

il p
....

l'a
....

Listen, repeat, and copy.

① l'idraulico
....

② il parrucchiere
....

③ la receptionist
....

④ il postino
....

⑤ l'addetta alle pulizie
....

Listen again and write the words.

r
....

la f
....

p
....

e
....

c
....

Listen, repeat, and copy.

① righe
....

② la fantasia
....

③ pois
....

④ economico
....

⑤ costoso
....

Day 5   What can you remember from this week?

1. Look at the pictures and circle the correct words.

1   spingere
    tirare

2   tenere
    fare cadere

3   sollevare
    spingere

4   fare cadere
    tirare

5   tenere
    sollevare

2. Look at the pictures and write the correct words.

1   r ....

2   €€€   c ....

3   p ....

4   la f ....

5   €   e ....

3. Look at the pictures and write the correct words.

il premio   prima   la competizione   secondo   terza

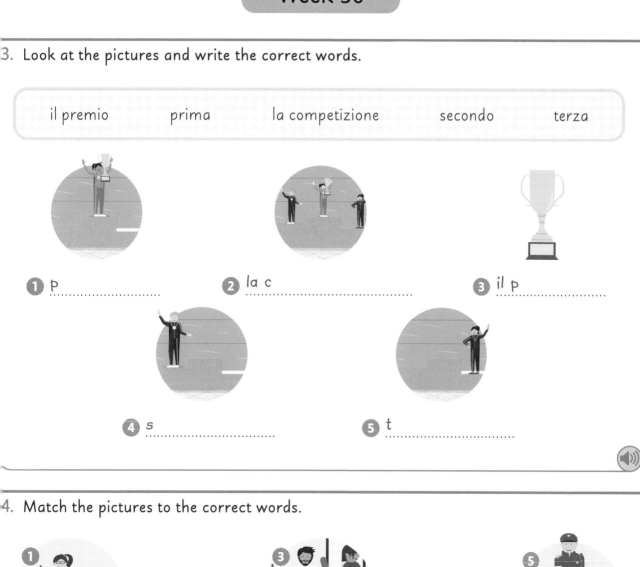

1 p ....

2 la c ....

3 il p ....

4 s ....

5 t ....

4. Match the pictures to the correct words.

il parrucchiere   il postino   l'addetta alle pulizie   la receptionist   l'idraulico

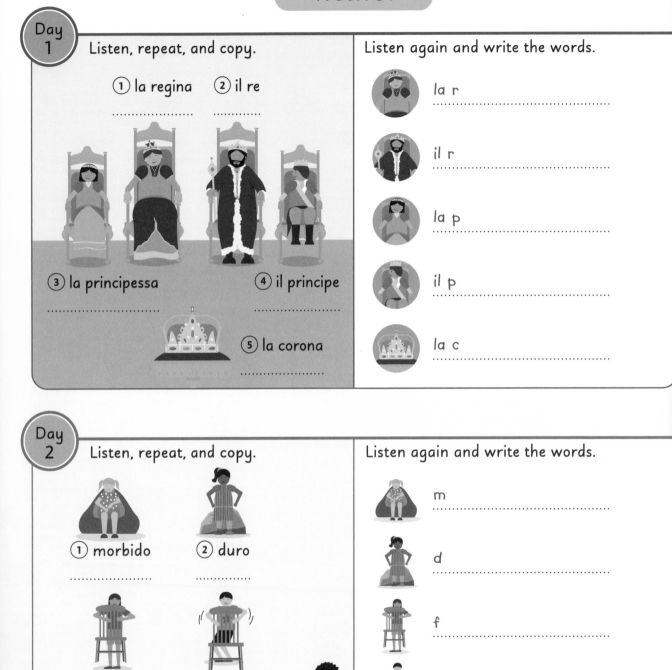

Day 1

Listen, repeat, and copy.

① la regina   ② il re

....

③ la principessa

....

④ il principe

....

⑤ la corona

....

Listen again and write the words.

la r ....

il r ....

la p ....

il p ....

la c ....

Day 2

Listen, repeat, and copy.

① morbido   ② duro

....

③ forte   ④ debole

....

⑤ rotto

....

Listen again and write the words.

m ....

d ....

f ....

d ....

r ....

Week 51

Listen again and write the words.

c ....

r ....

a ....

s ....

c ....

Listen, repeat, and copy.

① cercare

....

② riparare

....

③ accendere

....

④ spegnere

....

⑤ cambiare

....

Listen again and write the words.

la c ....

la c ....

il b ....

la t ....

la c ....

Listen, repeat, and copy.

① la cravatta

....

② la cerniera

....

③ il bottone

....

④ la tasca

....

⑤ la cintura

....

Week 51

Day 5

What can you remember from this week?

1. Look at the pictures and fill in the missing letters.

   c _ m _ i _ r _

   _ _ e _ c _ r _

   a _ c _ n _ e _ e

   _ p _ g _ e _ e

   r _ _ p _ r _ r _

2. Look at the pictures and circle the correct words.

la cravatta
il bottone

la tasca
il bottone

la cintura
la cerniera

la tasca
la cerniera

la cravatta
la cintura

3. Look at the pictures and write the letters in the correct order.

1 f t e o r

f _ _ _ _ _

2 m b i o d o r

m _ _ _ _ _ _ _

3 d r o u

d _ _ _ _

4 r t o o t

r _ _ _ _ _

5 d o e l e b

d _ _ _ _ _ _

4. Look at the pictures and mark the correct words.

1 la principessa ☐
la corona ☐

2 queen ☐
il re ☐

3 la principessa ☐
il principe ☐

4 la corona ☐
il re ☐

5 la regina ☐
il principe ☐

Week 52

Day 1

Listen, repeat, and copy.

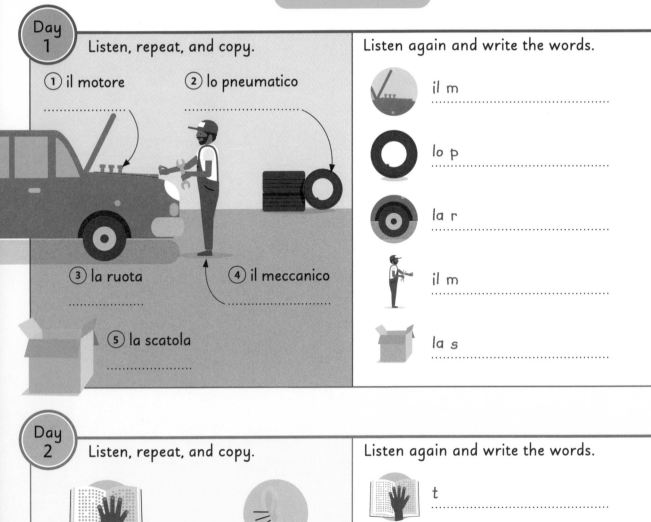

① il motore

② lo pneumatico

③ la ruota

④ il meccanico

⑤ la scatola

Listen again and write the words.

il m ....

lo p ....

la r ....

il m ....

la s ....

Day 2

Listen, repeat, and copy.

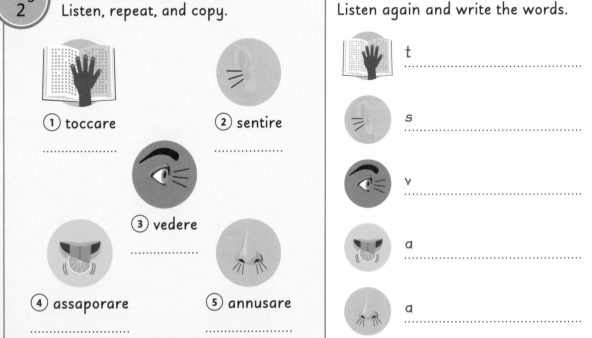

① toccare

② sentire

③ vedere

④ assaporare

⑤ annusare

Listen again and write the words.

t ....

s ....

v ....

a ....

a ....

Week 52

Listen again and write the words.

il v ....

il t ....

gli s ....

il c ....

la m ....

Listen, repeat, and copy.

① il violino

② il tamburo

....

③ gli strumenti

....

④ il concerto

....

⑤ la musica

....

Listen again and write the words.

la p ....

la p ....

il m ....

il p ....

il s ....

Listen, repeat, and copy.

① la pentola

....

② la padella

....

③ il microonde

....

④ il pepe

....

⑤ il sale

....

Day
5

What can you remember from this week?

1. Look at the pictures and write
   the correct words.

① il p ....

② il s ....

③ il m ....

④ la p ....

⑤ la p ....

2. Match the pictures to the correct words.

① la musica

② il tamburo

③ il violino

④ il concerto

⑤ gli strumenti

3. Look at the pictures and write the correct words.

toccare	assaporare	sentire	annusare	vedere

1 a ....

2 a ....

3 v ....

4 s ....

5 t ....

4. Read the words and mark the correct pictures.

1 il motore

A ☐　　B ☐

2 la ruota

A ☐　　B ☐

3 la scatola

A ☐　　B ☐

4 lo pneumatico

A ☐　　B ☐

5 il meccanico

A ☐　　B ☐

Numbers

Listen, repeat, and copy.

0 ① zero

10 ② dieci

20 ③ venti

30 ④ trenta

40 ⑤ quaranta

50 ⑥ cinquanta

60 ⑦ sessanta

70 ⑧ settanta

80 ⑨ ottanta

90 ⑩ novanta

91 ⑪ novantuno

92 ⑫ novantadue

93 ⑬ novantatré

94 ⑭ novantaquattro

95 ⑮ novantacinque

96 ⑯ novantasei

97 ⑰ novantasette

98 ⑱ novantotto

99 ⑲ novantanove

100 ⑳ cento

1 000 ㉑ mille

1 000 000 ㉒ un milione

Days

Listen, repeat, and copy.

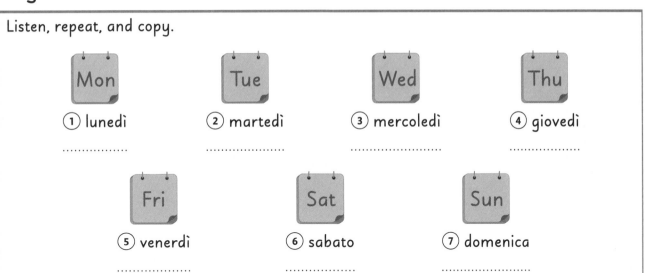

Mon
① lunedì
....

Tue
② martedì
....

Wed
③ mercoledì
....

Thu
④ giovedì
....

Fri
⑤ venerdì
....

Sat
⑥ sabato
....

Sun
⑦ domenica
....

Months

Listen, repeat, and copy

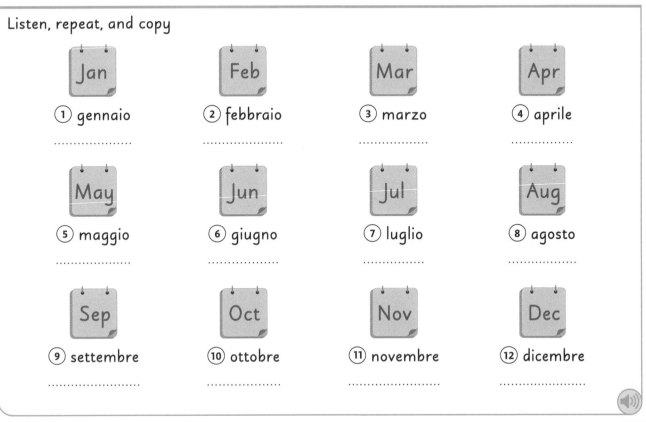

Jan
① gennaio
....

Feb
② febbraio
....

Mar
③ marzo
....

Apr
④ aprile
....

May
⑤ maggio
....

Jun
⑥ giugno
....

Jul
⑦ luglio
....

Aug
⑧ agosto
....

Sep
⑨ settembre
....

Oct
⑩ ottobre
....

Nov
⑪ novembre
....

Dec
⑫ dicembre
....

English word list

Each word is followed by the number of the week it appears in. For words that are not in a weekly unit, a page number is given (for example, **p216**).

KEY

adj	adjective
n	noun
num	number
prep	preposition
v	verb

A

act *v* 49
action figure *n* 2
actor *n* 43
add *v* 10
address *n* 30
aeroplane *n* 38
afraid *adj* 12
afternoon *n* 8
airport *n* 38
alphabet *n* 2
ambulance *n* 25
angry *adj* 12
animals *n* 10
answer *v* 5
ant *n* 17
apple *n* 1
apps *n* 21
April *n* **p217**
arm *n* 6
armchair *n* 7
arrive *v* 38
art *n* 44
artist *n* 48
ask *v* 17
asleep *adj* 40
astronaut *n* 34
aubergine *n* 23

August *n* **p217**
aunt *n* 14
autumn *n* 42
awake *adj* 40

B

baby *n* 7
back *adj* 40
back *n* 23
backpack *n* 5
badminton *n* 6
balcony *n* 12
ball *n* 6
balloon *n* 16
banana *n* 1
band *n* 41
bandage *n* 45
bank *n* 35
barn *n* 10
baseball *n* 6
baseball cap *n* 11
basement *n* 22
basket *n* 33
basketball *n* 6
bat *n* 15
bath *n* 26
bathroom *n* 4
beach *n* 15
beach ball *n* 43
beak *n* 47
beans *n* 29
bear *n* 8
beard *n* 40
beautiful *adj* 11
bed *n* 8
bedroom *n* 4
bee *n* 17
beetle *n* 39
behind *prep* 12
belt *n* 51
bench *n* 21
between *prep* 28
bicycle *n* 21

big *adj* 11
bin *n* 31
bird *n* 19
birthday party *n* 19
biscuit *n* 36
black *adj* 38
black *n* 4
blanket *n* 34
block of flats *n* 12
blonde *adj* 38
blue *n* 1
board *n* 1
board game *n* 2
boat *n* 27
body *n* 6
book *n* 5
bookcase *n* 7
bookshop *n* 21
boots *n* 26
bored *adj* 47
borrow *v* 35
bottle *n* 33
bottom *adj* 35
bounce *v* 9
bowl *n* 33
box *n* 52
boy *n* 7
bracelet *n* 48
branch *n* 13
brave *adj* 39
bread *n* 14
break *v* 40
breakfast *n* 12
bridge *n* 34
bring *v* 38
broken *adj* 51
bronze *n* 36
brother *n* 14
brown *adj* 38
brown *n* 4
brush *n* 37
brush my teeth *v* 25
bucket *n* 43
build *v* 44
burger *n* 7
burn *v* 45
bus *n* 24
bus station *n* 24
bus stop *n* 32

butter *n* 44
butterfly *n* 39
button *n* 51
buy *v* 43

C

cabbage *n* 23
café *n* 21
cake *n* 19
calendar *n* 8
camel *n* 24
camera *n* 34
camp *v* 45
candle *n* 19
car *n* 25
car park *n* 45
caravan *n* 42
card *n* 19
carpet *n* 19
carriage *n* 39
carrot *n* 15
carry *v* 43
cartoon *n* 46
castle *n* 27
cat *n* 6, 16
catch *v* 9
catch a bus *v* 13
caterpillar *n* 17
cave *n* 23
ceiling *n* 30
centre *n* 41
cereal *n* 12
chair *n* 16, 19
change *v* 51
charger *n* 31
chat *v* 45
cheap *adj* 50
cheese *n* 38
chef *n* 32
cherry *n* 20
chess *n* 45
chest *n* 20
chicken *n* 4
chicken *n* 7
child *n* 18
children *n* 10
chin *n* 40
chips *n* 7

chocolate n 44
choose v 17
chopsticks n 49
cinema n 21
circle n 17
circle v 10
circus n 28
city n 33
clap v 19
class n 1
classmate n 2
classroom n 2
claw n 47
clean adj 11
clean v 22
cleaner n 50
climb v 15
clock n 16, 42
close v 8
clothes n 7
cloud n 31
cloudy adj 28
clown n 28
coat n 26
coconut n 5
coffee n 36
cold adj 35
cold n 30
collar n 49
collect v 41
colour v 3
colours n 1
comb n 37
comet n 48
comic book n 46
compass n 48
competition n 50
complete v 29
computer n 28
concert n 52
cook v 16
cooker n 31
corner n 41
correct adj 22
cough n 30
count v 3
countryside n 30
cousin n 14
cow n 4

crab n 46
crayon n 2
crocodile n 24
cross v 10
crown n 51
cry v 26
cup n 33
cupboard n 31
curly adj 18
curtains n 43
cushion n 19
cut v 41
cycle v 13

D

dad n 3
dance v 11
dancing n 14
dark adj 40
date n 22
daughter n 3
day n 8
December n p217
deer n 46
dentist n 29
desert n 24
design n 47
design v 49
designer n 48
desk n 16
diary n 43
dictionary n 45
different adj 25
dining room n 4
dinner n 14
dinosaur n 10
dirty adj 11
do homework v 22
doctor n 18
dog n 6, 16
doll n 2
dolphin n 20
don't like v 37
donkey n 19
door n 30
downstairs n 22
dragonfly n 17
draw v 3

drawing n 14
dream v 25
dress n 9
drink v 16
drinks n 17
drive v 13
driver n 24
drop v 50
drum n 52
dry adj 35
dry v 16
duck n 37
DVD n 24

E

eagle n 47
ear n 11
earache n 30
Earth n 34
east n 48
eat v 16
e-book n 21
egg n 12
eight num 2
eighteen num 4
eighty num p216
elbow n 20
elephant n 5
eleven num 3
email n 21
email v 24
empty adj 46
engine n 52
engineer n 42
English n 44
entrance n 45
envelope n 30
evening n 8
excited adj 27
exit n 45
expensive adj 50
explore v 49
eye n 11
eyebrow n 40

F

face n 11
factory n 35
fall over v 26
family n 3
far adj 40
farm n 10
farmer n 19
fast adj 44
fat adj 44
father n 3
favourite adj 25
February n p217
feed v 40
feel v 52
fence n 14
festival n 41
fetch v 40
few adj 46
field n 10
fifteen num 3
fifty num p216
film n 21
film star n 21
find v 29
fingers n 20
finish v 33
fire n 42
fire engine n 25
fire station n 35
firefighter n 18
first adj 50
fish n 29
fish v 18
fishing n 29
fishing rod n 29
five num 1
fix v 44
flag n 43
flat n 12
floor n 30
flour n 44
flower n 13
fly n 39
fly v 18
fog n 13
foggy adj 28
food n 32
foot n 23

football *n* 23
forest *n* 27
fork *n* 49
forty *num* **p216**
four *num* 1
fourteen *num* 3
fox *n* 46
Friday *n* **p217**
fridge *n* 31
friendly *adj* 27
friends *n* 18
frog *n* 8, 37
front *adj* 40
fruit *n* 13
full *adj* 46
funfair *n* 28
fur *n* 49
furry *adj* 44

G

game *n* 16
garden *n* 14
garlic *n* 23
gate *n* 25
geography *n* 47
get dressed *v* 25
get off *v* 36
get on *v* 36
giraffe *n* 5
girl *n* 7
give *v* 38, 43
glass *n* 33
glasses *n* 37
gloves *n* 26
glue *n* 42
glue *v* 44
goat *n* 4
goggles *n* 22
gold *n* 36
goldfish *n* 6
golf *n* 23
gorilla *n* 26
granddaughter *n* 9
grandfather *n* 9
grandmother *n* 9
grandparents *n* 9
grandson *n* 9
grapes *n* 1

grass *n* 37
green *n* 1
greet *v* 38
grey *adj* 38
ground *n* 31
ground floor *n* 12
group *n* 18
grow *v* 41
grown-up *n* 18
gym *n* 31
gymnastics *n* 23

H

hair *n* 18
hairdresser *n* 50
half *adj* 46
half *n* 41
hall *n* 22
hand *n* 20
handbag *n* 48
happy *adj* 12
hard *adj* 51
hat *n* 41
head *n* 6
headache *n* 30
headphones *n* 31
hear *v* 52
helmet *n* 15
help *v* 26
hide *v* 40
hills *n* 30
hippo *n* 5
history *n* 47
hit *v* 9
hobbies *n* 14
hockey *n* 6
hockey stick *n* 36
hold *v* 50
holiday *n* 38
home *n* 14
honey *n* 44
hop *v* 32
horse *n* 4
hospital *n* 35
hot *adj* 35
hotel *n* 41
hour *n* 42
house *n* 3

hungry *adj* 27
hurry *v* 36
hurt *v* 26

I

ice *n* 32
ice cream *n* 28
ice hockey *n* 47
ice skates *n* 36
ice skating *n* 47
ill *adj* 39
in *prep* 12
in front of *prep* 12
insects *n* 31
inside *prep* 28
instruments *n* 52
invent *v* 49
invitation *n* 16
island *n* 15

J

jacket *n* 11
jam *n* 44
January *n* **p217**
jeans *n* 7
jellyfish *n* 20
jewellery *n* 37
jobs *n* 48
join *v* 29
journalist *n* 48
juice *n* 17
July *n* **p217**
jump *v* 15
jumper *n* 26
June *n* **p217**
jungle *n* 8

K

kangaroo *n* 26
key *n* 30
keyboard *n* 28
kick *n* 39
kick *v* 9
king *n* 51
kitchen *n* 4
kite *n* 6

kitten *n* 16
kiwi *n* 5
knee *n* 23
knife *n* 49

L

ladder *n* 25
ladybird *n* 17
lake *n* 27
lamp *n* 16
land *v* 36
languages *n* 47
laptop *n* 31
laugh *v* 45
leaf *n* 13
learn *v* 5
left *adj* 40
leg *n* 6
lemon *n* 20
lemonade *n* 17
lesson *n* 27
letter *n* 30
letters *n* 2
lettuce *n* 38
library *n* 31
life jacket *n* 29
lift *n* 12
lift *v* 50
light *adj* 40
lights *n* 19
like *v* 37
lime *n* 20
lion *n* 5
lips *n* 11
listen *v* 5
little *adj* 35
living room *n* 4
lizard *n* 23
long *adj* 18
look after *v* 40
look for *v* 51
lorry *n* 25
loud *adj* 40
lunch *n* 13

M

machine *n* 42
magazine *n* 46
make the bed *v* 25
man *n* 7
mango *n* 5
many *adj* 46
map *n* 45
March *n* **p217**
market *n* 30
mask *n* 45
mat *n* 25
match *n* 39
match *v* 10
maths *n* 44
May *n* **p217**
meal *n* 49
meat *n* 29
meatballs *n* 14
mechanic *n* 52
medicine *n* 45
meet *v* 34
men *n* 10
menu *n* 32
message *n* 21
metal *n* 49
microwave *n* 52
midday *n* 42
middle *adj* 35
midnight *n* 42
milk *n* 36
milkshake *n* 17
minute *n* 42
mirror *n* 26
mistake *n* 22
mix *v* 44
mobile phone *n* 31
Monday *n* **p217**
money *n* 33
monkey *n* 8
monster *n* 10
month *n* 43
moon *n* 34
morning *n* 8
mother *n* 3
motorbike *n* 25
mountain *n* 27
mouse *n* 16
mouse *n* 28

moustache *n* 40
mouth *n* 40
move *v* 19
mum *n* 3
museum *n* 33
mushroom *n* 23
music *n* 41, 52
musician *n* 41

N

name *n* 30
neck *n* 6
necklace *n* 48
nest *n* 47
net *n* 29
new *adj* 25
newspaper *n* 46
next to *prep* 12
nice *adj* 9
night *n* 8
nine *num* 2
nineteen *num* 4
ninety *num* **p216**
ninety-eight *num* **p216**
ninety-five *num* **p216**
ninety-four *num* **p216**
ninety-nine *num* **p216**
ninety-one *num* **p216**
ninety-seven *num* **p216**
ninety-six *num* **p216**
ninety-three *num* **p216**
ninety-two *num* **p216**
noisy *adj* 47
noodles *n* 7
north *n* 48
nose *n* 11
notepad *n* 45
November *n* **p217**
numbers *n* 2
nurse *n* 18

O

ocean *n* 15
October *n* **p217**
octopus *n* 20
office *n* 31
old *adj* 9, 25

olives *n* 38
on *prep* 12
one *num* 1
one hundred *num* **p216**
one million *num* **p216**
one thousand *num* **p216**
onion *n* 23
open *v* 8
orange *n* 1
orange *n* 4
order *v* 37
outside *prep* 28
oven *n* 31
over *prep* 28
owl *n* 46

P

paint *n* 2
paint *v* 44
painting *n* 14
pan *n* 52
pancake *n* 12
panda *n* 26
paper *n* 2
parent *n* 18
park *n* 3
parrot *n* 26
party *n* 16
passenger *n* 24
pasta *n* 14
path *n* 34
pattern *n* 50
paw *n* 49
pay *v* 37
peach *n* 20
pear *n* 5
peas *n* 15
pen *n* 2
pencil *n* 2
penguin *n* 37
people *n* 10
pepper *n* 15
pepper *n* 52
perfume *n* 37
person *n* 10
pets *n* 6
phone *v* 24
photo *n* 34

photographer *n* 48
pick up *v* 8
picnic *n* 34
picture *n* 27
pie *n* 29
pig *n* 19
pilot *n* 38
pineapple *n* 1
pink *n* 4
pizza *n* 7
planet *n* 48
plant *n* 13
plant *v* 41
plaster *n* 45
plastic *n* 49
plate *n* 33
platform *n* 39
play *v* 15, 32
play the guitar *v* 11
play the piano *v* 11
player *n* 39
playground *n* 3
plumber *n* 50
pocket *n* 51
point *v* 5
polar bear *n* 37
police officer *n* 18
pond *n* 37
pool *n* 41
pop star *n* 41
post office *n* 21
postcard *n* 34
poster *n* 8
postman *n* 50
pot *n* 52
potato *n* 15
practise *v* 22
prepare *v* 37
present *n* 19
pretty *adj* 9
prince *n* 51
princess *n* 51
printer *n* 28
prize *n* 50
project *n* 27
pull *v* 50
puppet *n* 2
puppy *n* 16
purple *n* 1

purse n 33
push v 50
put on v 17
puzzle n 27
puzzle book n 46
pyjamas n 7
pyramid n 24

Q
quarter n 41
queen n 51
question n 22
quiet adj 47

R
rabbit n 6
race n 36
race v 33
radio n 24
railway track n 39
rain n 13
rainbow n 13
read v 35
receptionist n 50
rectangle n 17
red adj 38
red n 1
reindeer n 37
relax v 22
remote control n 24
repair v 51
restaurant n 32
rhino n 26
rice n 29
ride n 28
ride a bike v 20
right adj 40
ring n 48
river n 23
road n 32
robot n 10
rock n 31
rocket n 34
rocks n 46
roller skates n 15
roof n 14
rubber n 5

rug n 7
ruler n 5
run v 13, 15

S
sad adj 12
sail v 18
salad n 38
salt n 52
same adj 25
sand n 15
sandals n 9
sandcastle n 43
sandwich n 13
Saturday n p217
sauce n 14
sausage n 12
scared adj 27
scarf n 26
scary adj 9
school n 3
science n 44
scissors n 5
score n 39
score v 20
screen n 28
sea n 6
seagull n 6
seal n 37
search v 29, 35
seasons n 42
seat n 21
seaweed n 46
second adj 50
see v 52
seesaw n 21
sell v 43
send v 24
sentence n 22
September n p217
seven num 2
seventeen num 4
seventy num p216
shapes n 17
shark n 20
shed n 14
sheep n 4
shelf n 26

shell n 46
ship n 6
shirt n 11
shoes n 9
shop v 17
shopping n 33
shopping centre n 45
shops n 45
short adj 18
shorts n 9
shoulder n 20
shout v 24
show v 34
shower n 26
sick adj 39
silver n 36
sing v 11
singer n 43
sink n 27
sister n 14
sit down v 8
six num 2
sixteen num 4
sixty num p216
skate v 20
skateboard n 10
skateboard v 20
ski v 20
skiing n 47
skip v 15
skirt n 11
skis n 36
sky n 31
skyscraper n 33
sledge n 36
sledging n 47
sleep v 45
slide n 21
slow adj 44
small adj 11
smell v 52
smile n 29
smoke n 42
snack n 13
snail n 39
snake n 24
snow n 32
snowball n 32
snowboard n 36

snowboarding n 47
snowflake n 32
snowman n 32
soap n 27
socks n 7
sofa n 7
soft adj 51
son n 3
sore adj 39
soup n 29
south n 48
space n 48
spade n 43
speak v 34
speakers n 24
spell v 3
spider n 39
spoon n 49
sports n 14
sports centre n 35
spots n 50
spring n 42
square n 17
squirrel n 46
stable n 19
stadium n 31
stage n 43
stairs n 22
stamp n 30
stand up v 8
starfish n 46
stars n 48
start v 33
station n 39
step n 25
stomach n 23
stomach-ache n 30
stone n 49
storm n 13
story n 27
straight adj 18
strawberry n 20
stream n 34
street n 3
stripes n 50
strong adj 51
student n 45
study v 35
subjects n 47

sugar n 36
suitcase n 38
summer n 42
sun n 34
sun lounger n 41
Sunday n p217
sunglasses n 41
sunny adj 28
supermarket n 31
surf v 18
surprised adj 12
swan n 37
sweets n 16
swim v 18
swimming n 22
swimming pool n 22
swimsuit n 22
swing n 21
swing v 32

T

table n 19
table tennis n 23
tablet n 21
tail n 49
take a photo v 11
take off v 36
talk v 24
tall adj 35
tap n 27
taste v 52
taxi n 24
tea n 36
teach v 5
teacher n 1
team n 39
teddy bear n 2
teeth n 29
telephone n 16
telescope n 48
television n 7
tell v 26
ten num 2, p216
tennis n 6
tennis racket n 15
tent n 42
theatre n 43
thin adj 44

think v 49
third adj 50
thirsty adj 27
thirteen num 3
thirty num p216
three num 1
throw v 9
Thursday n p217
tick v 10
ticket n 21
tidy adj 47
tidy v 22
tie n 51
tiger n 8
timetable n 44
tired adj 39
toes n 23
toilet n 26
tomato n 38
tongue n 29
toolbox n 42
tools n 42
tooth n 29
toothbrush n 27
toothpaste n 27
top adj 35
torch n 42
tortoise n 23
touch v 19
tour n 34
towel n 22
town n 21
toy box n 8
toys n 8
toyshop n 21
tractor n 10
traffic n 32
traffic lights n 32
train n 39
trainers n 15
travel v 34
tree n 13
triangle n 17
trolley n 33
trousers n 11
try v 29
T-shirt n 9
Tuesday n p217
turn v 32

turn off v 51
turn on v 51
TV n 24
twelve num 3
twenty num 4, p216
two num 1
tyre n 52

U

uncle n 14
under prep 28
underwear n 7
university n 33
untidy adj 47
upstairs n 22

V

vegetables n 15
vet n 18
video v 33
video game n 10
view n 34
village n 30
violin n 52
visit v 38
volleyball n 23

W

wait v 17
waiter n 32
wake up v 25
walk v 13, 19
wall n 25
walrus n 37
warm adj 35
wash v 16
watch n 48
watch v 33
water n 17
water v 41
waterfall n 23
watermelon n 5
wave n 15
wave v 19
weak adj 51
weather n 28

website n 31
Wednesday n p217
week n 43
weekend n 43
weigh v 43
west n 48
wet adj 35
whale n 20
wheel n 52
whiskers n 49
whisper v 35
whistle v 32
white n 4
whole n 41
wind n 13
window n 30
windy adj 28
wing n 47
winner n 36
winter n 42
wolf n 46
woman n 7
women n 10
wood n 30
wood n 49
wool n 49
words n 1
work v 34
write v 3

X

x-ray n 45

Y

year n 43
yellow n 1
yoghurt n 13
young adj 9

Z

zebra n 5
zebra crossing n 32
zero num p216
zip n 51
zoo n 33

Italian word list

Each word is followed by the number of the week it appears in. For words that are not in a weekly unit, a page number is given (for example, **p216**).

In Italian, all nouns (things or people) are either masculine or feminine (see p6). Adjectives (describing words) also change depending on whether the noun they are describing is masculine or feminine.
When two options for nouns or adjectives are given in the following list (for example, affamato / affamata), the masculine is given first.

KEY

adj	adjective
n	noun
num	number
prep	preposition
v	verb

A

abbinare *v* 10
accamparsi *v* 45
accendere *v* 51
accogliere *v* 38
l'acqua *n* 17
l'addetto alle pulizie /
   l'addetta alle pulizie *n* 50
addormentato /
   addormentata *adj* 40
l'adulto *n* 18
l'aeroplano *n* 38
l'aeroporto *n* 38
affamato / affamata *adj* 27
l'agenda *n* 43
l'agente di polizia *n* 18
aggiustare *v* 44
l'aglio *n* 23
agosto *n* **p217**
aiutare *v* 26
l'ala *n* 47
l'albergo *n* 41
l'albero *n* 13
l'alfabeto *n* 2
le alghe *n* 46
l'altalena *n* 21
l'altalena carosello *n* 21
alto / alta *adj* 35
gli altoparlanti *n* 24
alzarsi *v* 8
l'ambulanza *n* 25
amichevole *adj* 27
gli amici *n* 18
l'ananas *n* 1
andare in bicicletta *v* 13, 20
andare in skateboard *v* 20
l'anello *n* 48
l'angolo *n* 41
l'anguria *n* 5
gli animali *n* 10
gli animali domestici *n* 6

l'anno *n* 43
annoiato / annoiata *adj* 47
annusare *v* 52
l'ape *n* 17
l'appartamento *n* 12
applaudire *v* 19
le applicazioni *n* 21
aprile *n* **p217**
aprire *v* 8
l'aquila *n* 47
l'aquilone *n* 6
l'arancia *n* 1
arancione *n* 4
l'arcobaleno *n* 13
l'argento *n* 36
arrabbiato / arrabbiata *adj* 12
arrampicarsi *v* 15
arrivare *v* 38
arte e immagine *n* 44
l'artiglio *n* 47
l'artista *n* 48
l'ascensore *n* 12
l'asciugamano *n* 22
asciugare *v* 16
asciutto / asciutta *adj* 35
ascoltare *v* 5
l'asino *n* 19
aspettare *v* 17
assaporare *v* 52
assetato / assetata *adj* 27
l'astronauta *n* 34
atterrare *v* 36
l'attore / l'attrice *n* 43
gli attrezzi *n* 42
l'autista *n* 24
l'auto *n* 25
l'autobus *n* 24
l'autunno *n* 42

B

le bacchette *n* 49
i baffi *n* 49
il baffo *n* 40
bagnato / bagnata *adj* 35
il bagno *n* 4

il balcone *n* 12
la balena *n* 20
il bambino / la bambina /
   i bambini *n* 7, 10, 18
la bambola *n* 2
la banana *n* 1
la banca *n* 35
la bandiera *n* 43
il bar *n* 21
la barba *n* 40
la barca *n* 27
il baseball *n* 6
basso/bassa *adj* 35
il bebè *n* 7
il becco *n* 47
bello / bella *adj* 9, 11
bere *v* 16
la biancheria intima *n* 7
bianco *n* 4
le bibite *n* 17
la biblioteca *n* 31
il bicchiere *n* 33
la bicicletta *n* 21
il biglietto *n* 19
il biglietto *n* 21
il binario *n* 39
biondi *adj* 38
il biscotto *n* 36
blu *n* 1
la bocca *n* 40
la borsa *n* 48
il bosco *n* 30
la bottiglia *n* 33
il bottone *n* 51
il braccialetto *n* 48
il braccio *n* 6
il bronzo *n* 36
bruciare *v* 45
il bruco *n* 17
buono / buona *adj* 9
il burattino *n* 2
il burro *n* 44
la bussola *n* 48
la busta *n* 30

C

cadere v 26
il caffè n 36
calciare v 9
il calcio n 23
il calcio n 39
caldo / calda adj 35
il calendario n 8
i calzini n 7
cambiare v 51
la camera da letto n 4
il cameriere n 32
la camicia n 11
il camion n 25
il camion dei pompieri n 25
il cammello n 24
camminare v 13, 19
la campagna n 30
il campo n 10
cancellare v 10
il cancello n 25
la candela n 19
il cane n 6, 16
il canguro n 26
la canna da pesca n 29
il cantante / la cantante n 43
cantare v 11
il capanno n 14
i capelli n 18
il cappellino da baseball n 11
il cappello n 41
la capra n 4
le caramelle n 16
il caricabatterie n 31
la carne n 29
la carota n 15
il carrello n 33
la carrozza n 39
la carta n 2
la cartolina n 34
la casa n 3, 14
la cascata n 23
il casco n 15
la caserma dei pompieri n 35
la cassetta degli attrezzi n 42

castani adj 38
il castello n 27
il castello di sabbia n 43
il cavallo n 4
la caverna n 23
il cavolo n 23
il cellulare n 31
la cena n 14
cento num p216
centrale adj 35
il centro n 41
il centro commerciale n 45
il centro sportivo n 35
cercare v 29, 51
cerchiare v 10
il cerchio n 17
i cereali n 12
la cerniera n 51
il cerotto n 45
il cervo n 46
il cestino n 31
il cesto n 33
lo chef n 32
chiacchierare v 45
chiaro / chiara adj 40
la chiave n 30
chiedere v 17
la chiocciola n 39
chiudere v 8
il cibo n 32
il cielo n 31
il cigno n 37
la ciliegia n 20
il cinema n 21
cinquanta num p216
cinque num 1
la cintura n 51
il cioccolato n 44
la cipolla n 23
il circo n 28
la città n 21, 33
la classe n 1, 2
la coccinella n 17
il cocco n 5
il coccodrillo n 24

la coda n 49
la colazione n 12
la colla n 42
la collana n 48
il collare n 49
le colline n 30
il collo n 6
colorare v 3
i colori n 1
colpire v 9
il coltello n 49
coltivare v 41
la cometa n 48
il compagno di classe /
   la compagna di classe n 2
la competizione n 50
completare v 29
comprare v 43
il computer n 28, 31
il concerto n 52
la conchiglia n 46
il condominio n 12
il coniglio n 6
il contadino n 19
contare v 3
la coperta n 34
coraggioso / coraggiosa adj
   39
la corona n 51
il corpo n 6
correre v 13, 15
corti adj 18
il cortile n 3
costoso / costosa adj 50
costruire v 44
il costume da bagno n 22
la cravatta n 51
la credenza n 31
il cucchiaio n 49
il cucciolo n 16
la cucina n 4
cucinare v 16
le cuffie n 31
il cugino / la cugina n 14
il cuscino n 19

D

la danza n 14
danzare v 11
dare v 38, 43
dare da mangiare v 40
la data n 22
davanti prep 12
davanti adj 40
debole adj 51
decollare v 36
il delfino n 20
il denaro n 33
il dente n 29
i denti n 29
il dentifricio n 27
la dentista n 29
dentro prep 12
dentro prep 28
il deserto n 24
destra adj 40
dicembre n p217
diciannove num 4
diciassette num 4
diciotto num 4
dieci num 2, p216
dietro prep 12
dietro adj 40
il dinosauro n 10
disegnare v 3
il disegno n 14
di sopra adj 22
disordinato / disordinata adj
   47
di sotto adj 22
le dita dei piedi n 23
le dita della mano n 20
il divano n 7
diverso / diversa adj 25
il dizionario n 45
la doccia n 26
dodici num 3
dolorante adj 39
la domanda n 22
domenica n p217
la donna n 7

le donne *n* 10
dormire *v* 45
il dottore / la dottoressa *n* 18
due *num* 1
duro / dura *adj* 51
il dvd *n* 24

E

l'e-book *n* 21
economico / economica *adj* 50
l'elefante *n* 5
l'e-mail *n* 21
emozionato / emozionata *adj* 27
l'entrata *n* 45
l'erba *n* 37
l'errore *n* 22
esatto / esatta *adj* 22
esercitarsi *v* 22
esplorare *v* 49
L'Est *n* 48
l'estate *n* 42

F

la fabbrica *n* 35
i fagioli *n* 29
la famiglia *n* 3
la fantasia *n* 50
fare cadere *v* 50
fare i compiti *v* 22
fare una foto *v* 11
fare il letto *v* 25
far rimbalzare *v* 9
fare lo spelling *v* 3
fare spese *v* 17
fare surf *v* 18
la farfalla *n* 39
la farina *n* 44
farsi male *v* 26
la fasciatura *n* 45
la fattoria *n* 10
febbraio *n* p217
felice *adj* 12
la fermata dell'autobus *n* 32

la ferrovia *n* 39
la festa *n* 16
la festa di compleanno *n* 19
il festival *n* 41
il fienile *n* 10
la figlia / il figlio *n* 3
il film *n* 21
filmare *v* 33
il fine settimana *n* 43
la finestra *n* 30
finire *v* 33
il fiocco di neve *n* 32
il fiore *n* 13
fischiare *v* 32
il fiume *n* 23
la foca *n* 37
la foglia *n* 13
le forbici *n* 5
la forchetta *n* 49
la foresta *n* 27
il formaggio *n* 38
le forme *n* 17
la formica *n* 17
il fornello *n* 31
il forno *n* 31
forte *adj* 51
la foto *n* 27, 34
il fotografo / la fotografa *n* 48
il francobollo *n* 30
la fragola *n* 20
il frappè *n* 17
la frase *n* 22
il fratello *n* 14
freddo / fredda *adj* 35
il frigorifero *n* 31
la frutta *n* 13
il fumetto *n* 46
il fumo *n* 42
il fungo *n* 23
il fuoco *n* 42
fuori *prep* 28

G

il gabbiano *n* 6
la gallina *n* 4

la gamba *n* 6
la gara *n* 36
gareggiare *v* 33
il gattino *n* 16
il gatto *n* 6, 16
il gelato *n* 28
il genitore *n* 18
gennaio *n* p217
geografia *n* 47
il ghiaccio *n* 32
la giacca *n* 11
giallo *n* 1
il giardino *n* 14
la ginnastica artistica *n* 23
il ginocchio *n* 23
giocare *v* 15, 32
il giocatore *n* 39
i giocattoli *n* 8
il gioco *n* 16
il gioco da tavolo *n* 2
i gioielli *n* 37
il giornalista / la giornalista *n* 48
il giorno *n* 8
giovane *adj* 9
giovedì *n* p217
la giraffa *n* 5
girare *v* 32
il giubbotto *n* 26
giugno *n* p217
la giungla *n* 8
il golf *n* 23
il gomito *n* 20
la gomma *n* 5
la gonna *n* 11
il gorilla *n* 26
il granchio *n* 46
grande *adj* 11
grasso / grassa *adj* 44
il grattacielo *n* 33
gridare *v* 24
grigi *adj* 38
il gruppo *n* 18
il gruppo musicale *n* 41
i guanti *n* 26

guardare *v* 33
il gufo *n* 46
guidare *v* 13

H

l'hamburger *n* 7
gli hobby *n* 14
l'hockey *n* 6
l'hockey sul ghiaccio *n* 47

I

l'idraulico *n* 50
imparare *v* 5
impaurito / impaurita *adj* 12
incollare *v* 44
incontrare *v* 34
indicare *v* 5
l'indirizzo *n* 30
indossare *v* 17
inferiore *adj* 35
l'infermiere / l'infermiera *n* 18
inglese *n* 44
l'ingresso *n* 22
iniziare *v* 33
innaffiare *v* 41
l'insalata *n* 38
insegnare *v* 5
gli insetti *n* 31
l'intero *n* 41
inventare *v* 49
l'inverno *n* 42
inviare *v* 24
l'invito *n* 16
l'ippopotamo *n* 5
l'isola *n* 15

J

i jeans *n* 7

K

il kiwi *n* 5

L

le labbra *n* 11
il lago *n* 27
la lampada *n* 16
la lana *n* 49
lanciare *v* 9
il latte *n* 36
la lattuga *n* 38
la lavagna *n* 1
il lavandino *n* 27
lavare *v* 16
lavarsi i denti *v* 25
lavorare *v* 34
leggere *v* 35
il legno *n* 49
lento / lenta *adj* 44
il leone *n* 5
la lettera *n* 30
le lettere *n* 2
il lettino *n* 41
il letto *n* 8
la lezione *n* 27
la libellula *n* 17
la libreria *n* 7
la libreria *n* 21
il libro *n* 5
il lime *n* 20
la limonata *n* 17
il limone *n* 20
la lingua *n* 29
lingue straniere *n* 47
lisci *adj* 18
lontano / lontana *adj* 40
la lucertola *n* 23
le luci *n* 19
luglio *n* **p217**
la luna *n* 34
il luna park *n* 28
lunedì *n* **p217**
lunghi *adj* 18
il lupo *n* 46

M

la macchina *n* 42
la macchina fotografica *n* 34

la madre *n* 3
il maestro / la maestra *n* 1
maggio *n* **p217**
la maglietta *n* 9
il maglione *n* 26
magro / magra *adj* 44
il maiale *n* 19
malato / malata *adj* 39
il mal d'orecchi *n* 30
il mal di pancia *n* 30
il mal di testa *n* 30
mandare un'e-mail *v* 24
mangiare *v* 16
il mango *n* 5
la mano *n* 20
la mappa *n* 45
il mare *n* 6
la marmellata *n* 44
marrone *n* 4
martedì *n* **p217**
marzo *n* **p217**
la mascherina *n* 45
matematica *n* 44
le materie *n* 47
la matita *n* 2
la mattina *n* 8
la mazza *n* 15
la mazza da hockey *n* 36
il meccanico *n* 52
la medicina *n* 45
la medusa *n* 20
la mela *n* 1
la melanzana *n* 23
la mensola *n* 26
il mento *n* 40
il menù *n* 32
il mercato *n* 30
mercoledì *n* **p217**
mescolare *v* 44
il mese *n* 43
il messaggio *n* 21
la metà *n* 41
il metallo *n* 49
mettere in ordine *v* 22
la mezzanotte *n* 42

mezzo / mezza *adj* 46
il mezzogiorno *n* 42
il microonde *n* 52
il miele *n* 44
un milione *num* **p216**
mille *num* **p216**
il minuto *n* 42
molti / molte *adj* 46
la montagna *n* 27
la moquette *n* 19
morbido / morbida *adj* 51
la mosca *n* 39
mostrare *v* 34
il mostro *n* 10
la moto *n* 25
il motore *n* 52
il mouse *n* 28
la mucca *n* 4
muoversi *v* 19
il muro di cinta *n* 25
il museo *n* 33
la musica *n* 41, 52
il musicista / la musicista *n* 41

N

nascondersi *v* 40
il naso *n* 11
nauseato / nauseata *adj* 39
la nave *n* 6
navigare *v* 18
la nebbia *n* 13
nebbioso / nebbiosa *adj* 28
i negozi *n* 45
il negozio di giocattoli *n* 21
neri *adj* 38
nero *n* 4
la neve *n* 32
il nido *n* 47
il nipote / la nipote *n* 9
il nome *n* 30
non piacere *v* 37
il nonno/ la nonna / i nonni *n* 9
i noodle *n* 7
Il Nord *n* 38

la notte *n* 8
novanta *num* **p216**
novantacinque *num* **p216**
novantadue *num* **p216**
novantanove *num* **p216**
novantaquattro *num* **p216**
novantasei *num* **p216**
novantasette *num* **p216**
novantatré *num* **p216**
novantotto *num* **p216**
novantuno *num* **p216**
nove *num* 2
novembre *n* **p217**
i numeri *n* 2
nuotare *v* 18
il nuoto *n* 22
nuovo / nuova *adj* 25
la nuvola *n* 31
nuvoloso / nuvolosa *adj* 28

O

gli occhiali *n* 37
gli occhiali da sole *n* 41
gli occhialini *n* 22
l'occhio *n* 11
l'oceano *n* 15
le olive *n* 38
l'onda *n* 15
l'ora *n* 42
l'orario *n* 44
ordinare *v* 37
ordinato / ordinata *adj* 47
l'orecchio *n* 11
l'oro *n* 36
l'orologio *n* 16, 42, 48
l'orsetto *n* 2
l'orso *n* 8
l'orso polare *n* 37
oscillare *v* 32
l'ospedale *n* 35
ottanta *num* **p216**
otto *num* 2
ottobre *n* **p217**
L'Ovest *n* 48

227

P

la padella *n* 52
il padre *n* 3
il paese *n* 30
pagare *v* 37
il pagliaccio *n* 28
il palco *n* 43
la palestra *n* 31
la paletta *n* 43
la palla *n* 6
la pallacanestro *n* 6
la palla di neve *n* 32
la pallavolo *n* 23
il palloncino *n* 16
il pallone da spiaggia *n* 43
il pancake *n* 12
la panchina *n* 21
la pancia *n* 23
il panda *n* 26
il pane *n* 14
il panino *n* 13
il panorama *n* 34
i pantaloncini *n* 9
i pantaloni *n* 11
la papera *n* 37
il pappagallo *n* 26
il parcheggio *n* 45
il parco *n* 3
parlare *v* 24, 34
le parole *n* 1
il parrucchiere / la
    parrucchiera *n* 50
la partita *n* 39
il passeggero *n* 24
la pasta *n* 14
il pastello a cera *n* 2
il pasto *n* 49
la patata *n* 15
le patatine fritte *n* 7
il pattinaggio sul ghiaccio *n*
    47
pattinare sul ghiaccio *v* 20
i pattini a rotelle *n* 15
i pattini da ghiaccio *n* 36
pauroso / paurosa *adj* 9

il pavimento *n* 30
la pecora *n* 4
la pelliccia *n* 49
peloso / pelosa *adj* 44
la penna *n* 2
pensare *v* 49
la pentola *n* 52
il pepe *n* 52
il peperone *n* 15
la pera *n* 5
la persona *n* 10
le persone *n* 10
pesare *v* 43
la pesca *n* 20
la pesca *n* 29
pescare *v* 18
il pesce *n* 29
il pesce rosso *n* 6
il pettine *n* 37
il petto *n* 20
piacere *v* 37
il pianeta *n* 48
piangere *v* 26
il piano terra *n* 12
la pianta *n* 13
piantare *v* 41
il piatto *n* 33
piccolo / piccola *adj* 11
il picnic *n* 34
il piede *n* 23
pieno / piena *adj* 46
la pietra *n* 49
il pigiama *n* 7
il pilota *n* 38
il ping pong *n* 23
il pinguino *n* 37
la pioggia *n* 13
la piramide *n* 24
la piscina *n* 22, 41
i piselli *n* 15
la pittura *n* 2
la pittura *n* 14
pitturare *v* 44
la pizza *n* 7
la plastica *n* 49

lo pneumatico *n* 52
pochi / poche *adj* 46
pois *n* 50
il pollo *n* 7
le polpette *n* 14
il polpo *n* 20
la poltrona *n* 7
il pomeriggio *n* 8
il pomodoro *n* 38
il pompiere *n* 18
il ponte *n* 34
la pop star *n* 41
la porta *n* 30
il portafogli *n* 33
portare *v* 38, 43
il poster *n* 8
il postino / la postina *n* 50
il posto a sedere *n* 21
il pranzo *n* 13
preferito / preferita *adj* 25
il premio *n* 50
prendere *v* 9
prendere l'autobus *v* 13
prendersi cura *v* 40
preparare *v* 37
prestare *v* 35
la primavera *n* 42
primo / prima *adj* 50
il principe / la principessa *n*
    51
le professioni *n* 48
il profumo *n* 37
progettare *v* 49
il progetto *n* 27
provare *v* 29
pulire *v* 22
pulito / pulita *adj* 11
il punteggio *n* 39
il pupazzo di neve *n* 32
il puzzle *n* 27

Q

il quaderno *n* 45
il quadrato *n* 17
quaranta *num* p216

il quarto *n* 41
quattordici *num* 3
quattro *num* 1
quindici *num* 3
il quotidiano *n* 46

R

la racchetta da tennis *n* 15
raccogliere *v* 8
raccogliere *v* 41
raccontare *v* 26
la radio *n* 24
la radiografia *n* 45
il raffreddore *n* 30
il ragno *n* 39
il ramo *n* 13
la rana *n* 8, 37
il razzo *n* 34
il re *n* 51
il receptionist / la receptionist *n*
    50
recitare *v* 49
il regalo *n* 19
la regina *n* 51
la renna *n* 37
la rete *n* 29
il rettangolo *n* 17
ricci *adj* 18
ridere *v* 45
righe *n* 50
il righello *n* 5
rilassarsi *v* 22
il rinoceronte *n* 26
riparare *v* 51
riportare *v* 40
il riso *n* 29
rispondere *v* 5
il ristorante *n* 32
la rivista *n* 46
la rivista di enigmistica *n* 46
il robot *n* 10
le rocce *n* 46
la roccia *n* 31
rompere *v* 40
rosa *n* 4

rossi *adj* 38

rosso *n* 1

rotto / rotta *adj* 51

la roulotte *n* 42

rovistare *v* 35

il rubinetto *n* 27

rumoroso / rumorosa *adj* 40, 47

la ruota *n* 52

la ruota panoramica *n* 28

il ruscello *n* 34

S

sabato *n* p217

la sabbia *n* 15

la sala da pranzo *n* 4

il sale *n* 52

salire *v* 36

la salsiccia *n* 12

saltare *v* 15, 32

saltare la corda *v* 15

salutare *v* 19

il salvagente *n* 29

i sandali *n* 9

la saponetta *n* 27

sbrigarsi *v* 36

gli scacchi *n* 45

la scala *n* 25

le scale *n* 22

lo scalino *n* 25

lo scantinato *n* 22

lo scarabeo *n* 39

le scarpe *n* 9

le scarpe da ginnastica *n* 15

la scatola *n* 52

la scatola dei giocattoli *n* 8

scegliere *v* 17

scendere *v* 36

lo schermo *n* 28

la schiena *n* 23

gli sci *n* 36

lo sci *n* 47

sciare *v* 20

la sciarpa *n* 26

scienze *n* 44

la scimmia *n* 8

lo scivolo *n* 21

la scodella *n* 33

lo scoiattolo *n* 46

la scrivania *n* 16

scrivere *v* 3

la scuola *n* 3

scuro / scura *adj* 40

il secchiello *n* 43

secondo / seconda *adj* 50

sedersi *v* 8

la sedia *n* 16, 19

sedici *num* 4

segnare *v* 20

sei *num* 2

il semaforo *n* 32

il sentiero *n* 34

sentire *v* 52

la sera *n* 8

il serpente *n* 24

sessanta *num* p216

settanta *num* p216

sette *num* 2

settembre *n* p217

la settimana *n* 43

lo shopping *n* 33

sinistra *adj* 40

il sito web *n* 31

lo skateboard *n* 10

la slitta *n* 36

lo slittino *n* 47

lo snowboard *n* 36

lo snowboard *n* 47

il soffitto *n* 30

il soggiorno *n* 4

sognare *v* 25

il sole *n* 34

soleggiato / soleggiata *adj* 28

sollevare *v* 50

sommare *v* 10

sopra *prep* 12, 28

il sopracciglio *n* 40

la sorella *n* 14

sorpreso / sorpresa *adj* 12

il sorriso *n* 29

sotto *prep* 28

la spalla *n* 20

spaventato / spaventata *adj* 27

lo spazio *n* 48

la spazzola *n* 37

lo spazzolino *n* 27

lo specchio *n* 26

spegnere *v* 51

la spiaggia *n* 15

spingere *v* 50

sporco / sporca *adj* 11

gli sport *n* 14

spuntare *v* 10

lo spuntino *n* 13

la squadra *n* 39

lo squalo *n* 20

la staccionata *n* 14

lo stadio *n* 31

le stagioni *n* 42

lo stagno *n* 37

la stalla *n* 19

la stampante *n* 28

stanco / stanca *adj* 39

la statuetta *n* 2

la stazione *n* 39

la stazione degli autobus *n* 24

la stella del cinema *n* 21

la stella marina *n* 46

le stelle *n* 48

lo stilista / la stilista *n* 48

gli stivali *n* 26

la storia *n* 27

storia *n* 47

la strada *n* 3, 32

le strisce pedonali *n* 32

gli strumenti *n* 52

lo studente *n* 45

studiare *v* 35

il succo *n* 17

Il Sud *n* 48

il sugo *n* 14

suonare la chitarra *v* 11

suonare il pianoforte *v* 11

superiore *adj* 35

il supermercato *n* 31

sussurrare *v* 35

svegliarsi *v* 25

sveglio / sveglia *adj* 40

T

il tablet *n* 21

tagliare *v* 41

il tamburo *n* 52

il tappeto *n* 7

la tartaruga *n* 23

la tasca *n* 51

la tastiera *n* 28

il tavolo *n* 19

il taxi *n* 24

la tazza *n* 33

il tè *n* 36

il teatro *n* 43

il tecnico *n* 42

tecnologia *n* 47

il telecomando *n* 24

telefonare *v* 24

il telefono *n* 16

il telescopio *n* 48

la televisione *n* 7

la tempesta *n* 13

il tempo *n* 28

la tenda *n* 42

le tende *n* 43

tenere *v* 50

il tennis *n* 6

la terra *n* 34

il terreno *n* 31

terzo / terza *adj* 50

la testa *n* 6

il tetto *n* 14

la tigre *n* 8

tirare *v* 50

toccare *v* 19, 52

il topo *n* 16

la torcia *n* 42

torrido / torrida *adj* 35

la torta *n* 19, 29

la tosse *n* 30

tra *prep* **28**

il traffico *n* **32**

tranquillo / tranquilla *adj* **47**

il trattore *n* **10**

tre *num* **1**

tredici *num* **3**

il treno *n* **39**

trenta *num* **p216**

il triangolo *n* **17**

il tricheco *n* **37**

triste *adj* **12**

trovare *v* **29**

la tv *n* **24**

U

l'uccello *n* **19**

l'ufficio *n* **31**

l'ufficio postale *n* **21**

uguale *adj* **25**

undici *num* **3**

unire *v* **29**

l'università *n* **33**

uno *num* **1**

gli uomini *n* **10**

l'uomo *n* **7**

l'uovo *n* **12**

l'uscita *n* **45**

l'uva *n* **1**

V

la vacanza *n* **38**

la valigia *n* **38**

la vasca da bagno *n* **26**

vecchio / vecchia *adj* **9, 25**

vedere *v* **52**

veloce *adj* **44**

vendere *v* **43**

venerdì *n* **p216**

venti *num* **4, p216**

il vento *n* **13**

ventoso / ventosa *adj* **28**

verde *n* **1**

le verdure *n* **15**

vestirsi *v* **25**

i vestiti *n* **7**

il vestito *n* **9**

il veterinario / la veterinaria *n* **18**

viaggiare *v* **34**

il viaggio *n* **34**

vicino a *prep* **12**

il videogioco *n* **10**

la vignetta *n* **46**

il vincitore *n* **36**

viola *n* **1**

il violino *n* **52**

visitare *v* **38**

il viso *n* **11**

il volano *n* **6**

volare *v* **18**

la volpe *n* **46**

vuoto / vuota *adj* **46**

W

il water *n* **26**

Y

lo yogurt *n* **13**

Z

lo zaino *n* **5**

la zampa *n* **49**

la zebra *n* **5**

lo zerbino *n* **25**

zero *num* **p216**

lo zio / la zio *n* **14**

lo zoo *n* **33**

lo zucchero *n* **36**

la zuppa *n* **29**

Common subjects

This is an index of common topics found in the book. Each subject is followed by the weeks it is taught in or the page number it appears on (for example, p216).

animals
4, 5, 6, 8, 16, 17, 19, 20, 23, 24, 26, 37, 39, 46, 47, 49

body
6, 11, 18, 20, 23, 29, 38, 40

clothes
7, 9, 11, 15, 26, 51

directions
12, 28, 40, 48

family
3, 9, 14

feelings
12, 27

food and drink
1, 5, 7, 12, 13, 14, 15, 16, 17, 20, 23, 29, 36, 38, 44, 49, 52

health
30, 39, 45

hobbies
11, 14, 15, 18, 20, 21, 22, 29, 32, 36, 41, 43, 44, 46, 47, 49, 52

holidays
6, 11, 15, 34, 38, 41, 42, 43, 45

home
4, 7, 8, 12, 14, 16, 19, 22, 24, 25, 26, 27, 30, 31, 33, 37, 52

jobs
18, 29, 34, 41, 42, 43, 48, 50

nature
13, 15, 23, 24, 27, 30, 31, 37, 41, 42, 46

numbers
1, 2, 3, 4, p216

people
7, 10, 18, 51

places
3, 10, 21, 24, 27, 28, 30, 31, 32, 33, 34, 35, 45

school
1, 2, 3, 5, 8, 10, 22, 27, 35, 44, 45, 47

shapes and colours
1, 4, 17

space
34, 48

sports
6, 9, 15, 20, 22, 23, 33, 36, 39, 47, 50

technology
21, 24, 28, 31, 42

time
8, 42, 43, p217

toys
2, 8, 10

transport
13, 24, 25, 32, 36, 38, 39, 52

weather
13, 28, 32, 35

Answers

Week 1

1
1. il maestro
2. la lavagna
3. i colori
4. le parole
5. la classe

2
1. viola
2. rosso
3. giallo
4. blu
5. verde

3
1. due
2. cinque
3. quattro
4. uno
5. tre

4
1. l'ananas
2. l'uva
3. la mela
4. la banana
5. l'arancia

Week 2

1
1. i numeri
2. l'alfabeto
3. le lettere
4. la compagna di classe
5. la classe

2
1. la bambola
2. la statuetta
3. l'orsetto
4. il gioco da tavolo
5. il burattino

3
1. B   2. A   3. B   4. A
5. A

4
1. otto
2. sei
3. nove
4. sette
5. dieci

Week 3

1
1. disegnare
2. colorare
3. contare
4. fare lo spelling
5. scrivere

2
1. la scuola
2. il cortile
3. il parco
4. la strada
5. la casa

3
1. undici
2. tredici
3. quindici
4. quattordici
5. dodici

4
1. la famiglia
2. il padre
3. la madre
4. il figlio
5. la figlia

Week 4

1
1. marrone
2. rosa
3. arancione
4. bianco
5. nero

2
1. B   2. A   3. B   4. A
5. A

3
1. la gallina
2. la capra
3. la pecora
4. la mucca
5. il cavallo

4
1. diciassette
2. venti
3. diciotto
4. sedici
5. diciannove

Week 5

1
1. la zebra
2. l'ippopotamo
3. il leone
4. la giraffa
5. l'elefante

2
1. le forbici
2. il libro
3. il righello
4. la gomma
5. lo zaino

3
1. ascoltare
2. insegnare
3. imparare
4. indicare
5. rispondere

4
1. il kiwi
2. la pera
3. l'anguria
4. il cocco
5. il mango

Week 6

1
1. B   2. A   3. B   4. A
5. B

2
1. la testa
2. la gamba
3. il corpo
4. il braccio
5. il collo

3
1. l'hockey
2. il tennis
3. il baseball
4. la pallacanestro
5. il volano

4
1. il mare
2. il gabbiano
3. l'aquilone
4. la nave
5. la palla

Week 7

1
1. la bambina
2. l'uomo
3. il bambino
4. il bebè
5. la donna

2
1. B 2. A 3. A 4. B
5. A

3
1. il divano
2. il tappeto
3. la poltrona
4. la libreria
5. la televisione

4
1. la pizza
2. i noodle
3. l'hamburger
4. le patatine fritte
5. il pollo

Week 8

1
1. la tigre
2. la rana
3. la scimmia
4. la giungla
5. l'orso

2
1. A 2. B 3. A 4. A
5. B

3
1. sedersi
2. aprire
3. chiudere
4. raccogliere
5. alzarsi

4
1. il pomeriggio
2. la notte
3. la mattina
4. la sera
5. il giorno

Week 9

1
1. i nonni
2. la nonna
3. il nonno
4. il nipote
5. la nipote

2
1. la maglietta
2. il vestito
3. i sandali
4. le scarpe
5. i pantaloncini

3
1. bello
2. vecchio
3. pauroso
4. giovane
5. buono

4
1. prendere
2. colpire
3. calciare
4. lanciare
5. far rimbalzare

Week 10

1
1. la persona
2. le donne
3. i bambini
4. le persone
5. gli uomini

2
1. B 2. A 3. B 4. A
5. A

3
1. il trattore
2. il campo
3. la fattoria
4. gli animali
5. il fienile

4
1. il dinosauro
2. lo skateboard
3. il videogioco
4. il robot
5. il mostro

Week 11

1
1. l'occhio
2. le labbra
3. il naso
4. l'orecchio
5. il viso

2
1. A 2. B 3. A 4. A
5. B

3
1. bello
2. pulito
3. piccolo
4. sporco
5. grande

4
1. la camicia
2. il cappellino da baseball
3. la gonna
4. i pantaloni
5. la giacca

Week 12

1
1. dentro
2. davanti
3. dietro
4. vicino a
5. sopra

2
1. i cereali
2. la colazione
3. l'uovo
4. il pancake
5. la salsiccia

3
1. il balcone
2. l'ascensore
3. il condominio
4. il piano terra
5. l'appartamento

4
1. sorpresa
2. triste
3. impaurito
4. felice
5. arrabbiata

Week 13

1
1. A 2. A 3. B 4. A
5. B

2
1. la foglia
2. il ramo
3. l'albero
4. la pianta
5. il fiore

3

1 la tempesta
2 il vento
3 la nebbia
4 la pioggia
5 l'arcobaleno

4

1 lo spuntino
2 lo yogurt
3 la frutta
4 il panino
5 il pranzo

Week 14

1

1 il tetto
2 la staccionata
3 il giardino
4 il capanno
5 la casa

2

1 il disegno
2 la danza
3 la pittura
4 gli sport
5 gli hobby

3

1 lo zio
2 la zia
3 la cugina
4 il fratello
5 la sorella

4

1 la pasta
2 il sugo
3 la cena
4 il pane
5 le polpette

Week 15

1

1 la carota
2 i piselli
3 le verdure
4 la patata
5 il peperone

2

1 l'oceano
2 l'onda
3 la spiaggia
4 la sabbia
5 l'isola

3

1 il casco
2 le scarpe da ginnastica
3 la mazza
4 la racchetta da tennis
5 i pattini a rotelle

4

1 correre
2 saltare la corda
3 giocare
4 arrampicarsi
5 saltare

Week 16

1

1 le caramelle
2 la festa
3 il gioco
4 l'invito
5 il palloncino

2

1 cucinare
2 mangiare
3 lavare
4 asciugare
5 bere

3

1 il gatto
2 il topo
3 il cane
4 il cucciolo
5 il gattino

4

1 la lampada
2 l'orologio
3 il telefono
4 la scrivania
5 la sedia

Week 17

1

1 chiedere
2 scegliere
3 aspettare
4 indossare
5 fare spese

2

1 la coccinella
2 l'ape
3 la formica
4 la libellula
5 il bruco

3

1 il succo
2 le bibite
3 l'acqua
4 la limonata
5 il frappè

4

1 il triangolo
2 il cerchio
3 il rettangolo
4 il quadrato
5 le forme

Week 18

1

1 A 2 B 3 B 4 A
5 B

2

1 i capelli
2 corti
3 lunghi
4 lisci
5 ricci

3

1 fare surf
2 pescare
3 volare
4 nuotare
5 navigare

4

1 il bambino
2 l'adulto
3 il genitore
4 il gruppo
5 gli amici

Week 19

1

1 muoversi
2 camminare
3 toccare
4 applaudire
5 salutare

2

1 l'uccello
2 l'asino
3 la stalla
4 il maiale
5 il contadino

3

1. il regalo
2. il biglietto
3. la festa di compleanno
4. la candela
5. la torta

4

1. la moquette
2. il cuscino
3. le luci
4. la sedia
5. il tavolo

Week 20

1

1. A 2. B 3. A 4. B
5. A

2

1. il delfino
2. la medusa
3. il polpo
4. lo squalo
5. la balena

3

1. le dita della mano
2. la spalla
3. il gomito
4. la mano
5. il petto

4

1. il limone
2. la ciliegia
3. la fragola
4. la pesca
5. il lime

Week 21

1

1. il tablet
2. l'e-book
3. il messaggio
4. le applicazioni
5. l'e-mail

2

1. la libreria
2. l'ufficio postale
3. il negozio di giocattoli
4. il bar
5. la città

3

1. il posto a sedere
2. il cinema
3. la stella del cinema
4. il biglietto
5. il film

4

1. A 2. B 3. A 4. A
5. B

Week 22

1

1. l'ingresso
2. di sopra
3. di sotto
4. le scale
5. lo scantinato

2

1. fare i compiti
2. mettere in ordine
3. esercitarsi
4. rilassarsi
5. pulire

3

1. l'asciugamano
2. la piscina
3. il costume da bagno
4. gli occhialini
5. il nuoto

4

1. esatto
2. la domanda
3. la data
4. l'errore
5. la frase

Week 23

1

1. la cipolla
2. l'aglio
3. il cavolo
4. il fungo
5. la melanzana

2

1. il fiume
2. la cascata
3. la caverna
4. la lucertola
5. la tartaruga

3

1. il golf
2. la pallavolo
3. la ginnastica artistica
4. il ping pong
5. il calcio

4

1. la schiena
2. la pancia
3. il ginocchio
4. il piede
5. le dita dei piedi

Week 24

1

1. A 2. B 3. B 4. A
5. B

2

1. il cammello
2. la piramide
3. il deserto
4. il serpente
5. il coccodrillo

3

1. il taxi
2. il passeggero
3. l'autobus
4. l'autista
5. la stazione degli autobus

4

1. telefonare
2. mandare un'e-mail
3. inviare
4. gridare
5. parlare

Week 25

1

1. lo scalino
2. lo zerbino
3. il muro di cinta
4. la scala
5. il cancello

2

1. l'auto
2. il camion
3. la moto
4. il camion dei pompieri
5. l'ambulanza

3

1. B 2. A 3. A 4. B
5. A

4
1. uguale
2. diverso
3. nuovo
4. preferito
5. vecchio

Week 26
1
1. raccontare
2. piangere
3. aiutare
4. farsi male
5. cadere

2
1. il canguro
2. il gorilla
3. il rinoceronte
4. il panda
5. il pappagallo

3
1. gli stivali
2. il maglione
3. la sciarpa
4. il giubbotto
5. i guanti

4
1. la vasca da bagno
2. il water
3. lo specchio
4. la mensola
5. la doccia

Week 27
1
1. spaventato
2. emozionata
3. amichevole
4. assetato
5. affamato

2
1. la saponetta
2. il lavandino
3. il dentifricio
4. lo spazzolino
5. il rubinetto

3
1. il progetto
2. il puzzle
3. la foto
4. la storia
5. la lezione

4
1. la foresta
2. la montagna
3. il castello
4. il lago
5. la barca

Week 28
1
1. A 2. B 3. B 4. A
5. B

2
1. nebbioso
2. soleggiato
3. il tempo
4. ventoso
5. nuvoloso

3
1. il mouse
2. la stampante
3. il computer
4. lo schermo
5. la tastiera

4
1. il circo
2. la ruota panoramica
3. il gelato
4. il luna park
5. il pagliaccio

Week 29
1
1. cercare
2. trovare
3. unire
4. completare
5. provare

2
1. il pesce
2. la pesca
3. la canna da pesca
4. la rete
5. il salvagente

3
1. i denti
2. la lingua
3. il dente
4. il sorriso
5. la dentista

4
1. i fagioli
2. la carne
3. il riso
4. la zuppa
5. la torta

Week 30
1
1. il paese
2. le colline
3. la campagna
4. il bosco
5. il mercato

2
1. la lettera
2. l'indirizzo
3. la busta
4. il francobollo
5. il nome

3
1. B 2. A 3. B 4. A
5. B

4
1. il soffitto
2. la finestra
3. la porta
4. il pavimento
5. la chiave

Week 31
1
1. B 2. B 3. B 4. A
5. A

2
1. l'ufficio
2. la biblioteca
3. lo stadio
4. la palestra
5. il supermercato

3
1. il fornello
2. il cestino
3. il forno
4. la credenza
5. il frigorifero

4
1. la roccia
2. il cielo
3. la nuvola
4. il terreno
5. gli insetti

Week 32
1
1. B 2. A 3. A 4. A
5. B

236

2
1. il menù
2. il ristorante
3. lo chef
4. il cibo
5. il cameriere

3
1. giocare
2. saltare
3. girare
4. oscillare
5. fischiare

4
1. la strada
2. la fermata dell'autobus
3. il traffico
4. le strisce pedonali
5. il semaforo

Week 33

1
1. il piatto
2. la bottiglia
3. il bicchiere
4. la scodella
5. la tazza

2
1. A 2. B 3. A 4. A
5. B

3
1. il portafogli
2. lo shopping
3. il cesto
4. il denaro
5. il carrello

4
1. lo zoo
2. la città
3. il museo
4. l'università
5. il grattacielo

Week 34

1
1. viaggiare
2. lavorare
3. parlare
4. incontrare
5. mostrare

2
1. l'astronauta
2. la terra
3. il sole
4. la luna
5. il razzo

3
1. il ponte
2. il ruscello
3. il sentiero
4. il picnic
5. la coperta

4
1. la foto
2. il panorama
3. la macchina fotografica
4. il viaggio
5. la cartolina

Week 35

1
1. B 2. A 3. A 4. A
5. B

2
1. bassa
2. inferiore
3. centrale
4. alto
5. superiore

3
1. caldo
2. asciutto
3. bagnata
4. freddo
5. torrido

4
1. studiare
2. sussurrare
3. rovistare
4. leggere
5. prestare

Week 36

1
1. il tè
2. il biscotto
3. il caffè
4. il latte
5. lo zucchero

2
1. l'oro
2. il vincitore
3. l'argento
4. il bronzo
5. la gara

3
1. decollare
2. atterrare
3. sbrigarsi
4. scendere
5. salire

4
1. B 2. A 3. A 4. B
5. A

Week 37

1
1. piacere
2. non piacere
3. pagare
4. ordinare
5. preparare

2
1. il pettine
2. gli occhiali
3. la spazzola
4. il profumo
5. i gioielli

3
1. il pinguino
2. l'orso polare
3. la foca
4. la renna
5. il tricheco

4
1. l'erba
2. la rana
3. lo stagno
4. il cigno
5. la papera

Week 38

1
1. il pilota
2. l'aeroporto
3. la vacanza
4. la valigia
5. l'aeroplano

2
1. portare
2. arrivare
3. visitare
4. dare
5. accogliere

3

1. castani
2. biondi
3. rossi
4. neri
5. grigi

4

1. l'insalata
2. la lattuga
3. il pomodoro
4. il formaggio
5. le olive

Week 39

1

1. la partita
2. il calcio
3. la squadra
4. il punteggio
5. il giocatore

2

1. lo scarabeo
2. la mosca
3. la farfalla
4. la chiocciola
5. il ragno

3

1. coraggioso
2. nauseata
3. dolorante
4. stanco
5. malato

4

1. B 2. A 3. B 4. B
5. A

Week 40

1

1. chiaro
2. sveglio
3. scuro
4. addormentato
5. rumoroso

2

1. nascondersi
2. riportare
3. dare da mangiare
4. rompere
5. prendersi cura

3

1. lontana
2. sinistra
3. dietro
4. destra
5. davanti

4

1. la bocca
2. il mento
3. il sopracciglio
4. il baffo
5. la barba

Week 41

1

1. l'intero
2. l'angolo
3. la metà
4. il centro
5. il quarto

2

1. la piscina
2. il cappello
3. l'albergo
4. il lettino
5. gli occhiali da sole

3

1. B 2. A 3. B 4. A
5. A

4

1. raccogliere
2. piantare
3. innaffiare
4. coltivare
5. tagliare

Week 42

1

1. l'orologio
2. il mezzogiorno
3. il minuto
4. la mezzanotte
5. l'ora

2

1. il fuoco
2. la roulotte
3. la tenda
4. la torcia
5. il fumo

3

1. l'estate
2. l'inverno
3. l'autunno
4. la primavera
5. le stagioni

4

1. la colla
2. il tecnico
3. la cassetta degli attrezzi
4. gli attrezzi
5. la macchina

Week 43

1

1. pesare
2. comprare
3. dare
4. vendere
5. portare

2

1. l'attore
2. le tende
3. il palco
4. la cantante
5. il teatro

3

1. la bandiera
2. il pallone da spiaggia
3. il secchiello
4. la paletta
5. il castello di sabbia

4

1. il mese
2. la settimana
3. l'anno
4. l'agenda
5. il fine settimana

Week 44

1

1. arte e immagine
2. matematica
3. scienze
4. inglese
5. l'orario

2

1. costruire
2. pitturare
3. mescolare
4. aggiustare
5. incollare

3

1. il burro
2. la marmellata
3. il cioccolato
4. la farina
5. il miele

4

1. peloso
2. lento
3. grasso
4. veloce
5. magro

Week 45

1

1. l'uscita
2. il parcheggio
3. i negozi
4. l'entrata
5. il centro commerciale

2

1. lo studente
2. la mappa
3. gli scacchi
4. il dizionario
5. il quaderno

3

1. la medicina
2. la radiografia
3. la fasciatura
4. il cerotto
5. la mascherina

4

1. bruciare
2. ridere
3. chiacchierare
4. accamparsi
5. dormire

Week 46

1

1. il lupo
2. il gufo
3. il cervo
4. lo scoiattolo
5. la volpe

2

1. il granchio
2. la conchiglia
3. le rocce
4. le alghe
5. la stella marina

3

1. pieno
2. vuoto
3. mezzo
4. pochi
5. molti

4

1. A 2. B 3. B 4. B
5. A

Week 47

1

1. geografia
2. tecnologia
3. storia
4. lingue straniere
5. le materie

2

1. il nido
2. il becco
3. l'ala
4. l'artiglio
5. l'aquila

3

1. rumoroso
2. tranquilla
3. disordinata
4. ordinata
5. annoiato

4

1. A 2. B 3. A 4. B
5. B

Week 48

1

1. la bussola
2. Il Nord
3. L'Ovest
4. L'Est
5. Il Sud

2

1. le professioni
2. la stilista
3. il giornalista
4. l'artista
5. la fotografa

3

1. l'anello
2. il braccialetto
3. la borsa
4. la collana
5. l'orologio

4

1. la cometa
2. lo spazio
3. il pianeta
4. le stelle
5. il telescopio

Week 49

1

1. B 2. A 3. B 4. A
5. B

2

1. il metallo
2. la pietra
3. il legno
4. la plastica
5. la lana

3

1. i baffi
2. la zampa
3. la coda
4. il collare
5. la pelliccia

4

1. inventare
2. pensare
3. esplorare
4. recitare
5. progettare

Week 50

1

1. tirare
2. tenere
3. spingere
4. fare cadere
5. sollevare

2

1. righe
2. costoso
3. pois
4. la fantasia
5. economico

3

1. prima
2. la competizione
3. il premio
4. secondo
5. terza

4
1. l'addetta alle pulizie
2. la receptionist
3. il parrucchiere
4. l'idraulico
5. il postino

Week 51

1
1. cambiare
2. cercare
3. accendere
4. spegnere
5. riparare

2
1. la cravatta
2. il bottone
3. la cerniera
4. la tasca
5. la cintura

3
1. forte
2. morbido
3. duro
4. rotto
5. debole

4
1. la principessa
2. il re
3. il principe
4. la corona
5. la regina

Week 52

1
1. il pepe
2. il sale
3. il microonde
4. la pentola
5. la padella

2
1. il tamburo
2. la musica
3. il concerto
4. gli strumenti
5. il violino

3
1. assaporare
2. annusare
3. vedere
4. sentire
5. toccare

4
1. B 2. A 3. B 4. A
5. B

Acknowledgments

The publisher would like to thank:

Adam Brackenbury for design and illustration assistance; Edwood Burn for illustration assistance; Ankita Awasthi Tröger and Andiamo! Language Services Ltd for proofreading; Abigail Ellis for indexing; ID Audio for audio recording and production; Christine Stroyan and Sophie Adam for audio recording management; and Rakesh Kumar, Priyanka Sharma, and Saloni Singh for jacket design assistance.

All images are copyright DK. For more information, please visit **www.dkimages.com**.